SNOWMAN

By RUTHERFORD MONTGOMERY

SNOWMAN
THE CAPTURE OF WEST WIND
KLEPTY
BEAVER WATER
CARCAJOU
WAPITI THE ELK
MOUNTAIN MAN
HILL RANCH
A HORSE FOR CLAUDIA AND DENNIS (*with Natlee Kenoyer*)
TOM PITTMAN, USAF
JETS AWAY
OUT OF THE SUN
WAR WINGS
THUMBS UP

The Kent Barstow Adventure Stories

KENT BARSTOW: SPECIAL AGENT
MISSILE AWAY
MISSION INTRUDER
KENT BARSTOW: SPACE MAN

The Golden Stallion Series

RUTHERFORD MONTGOMERY

SNOWMAN

MEREDITH PRESS / New York

Fourth Printing, November, 1967

Library of Congress Catalogue Card Number: 62-8535

MANUFACTURED IN THE UNITED STATES OF AMERICA FOR MEREDITH PRESS

VAN REES PRESS • NEW YORK

Foreword

IN writing *Snowman* I have tried to be as accurate as possible concerning names and places, events at the horse shows and elsewhere.

I have taken only one liberty and that is in the description of the National Horse Show in Madison Square Garden. Here I have combined certain elements from the 1958 and the 1959 shows, rather than describe both shows. The events selected are accurate, but did not all happen at the same show.

RUTHERFORD MONTGOMERY

Los Gatos, California
September 15, 1961

PUBLISHER'S NOTE

UNFORTUNATELY, when Snowman was a plow horse and in the early days after he was bought by Harry de Leyer, no one was taking pictures of him. It was not until he became famous that the photographers discovered him. As a result the pictures we have used do not always literally illustrate the text. But they are of course pictures of Snowman, and we hope they illustrate the spirit, if not the letter, of Mr. Montgomery's story.

The pictures on pages 17, 29-30, and 43 are used through the courtesy of Mr. de Leyer. All the other pictures are used through the courtesy of Budd Studios.

Contents

SNOWMAN

1 | End of the Road

EVERY Monday during the year there is a horse auction held at New Holland, Pennsylvania. Horses are brought from near and far to be sold to the highest bidder. For some of the horses this means a better home; for others it is a step down. No longer wanted or needed, they are sold, their owners not caring about who buys them or why. For a few it is the end, a ride in a truck to where they will, in a few days, be processed into dog food to fill some of the million cans with gaily decorated labels that reach thousands of supermarket shelves across the land.

The auction sale was well under way one wintry Monday in February, 1956. The auctioneer pounded his hammer on his high desk as a tall chestnut gelding danced into the ring, ridden by a stable hand. His handler had trouble bringing him up and turning him around so that the buyers could check his good points. The tall chestnut had good points. It was clear that he was a thoroughbred, a high-strung, spirited animal. The trained horsemen in the crowd knew at once that here was a horse that had given his owner trouble. He was most certainly a show horse, possibly a hunter who had gone bad, become unmanageable, perhaps even dangerous. He certainly had a bad record or he wouldn't be up for sale as a discard, with his owner not caring who got him.

"Here is a fine show horse," the auctioneer announced. "A spirited animal anyone would be proud to own and show. Buy him and make a jumper or a hunter out of him, perhaps a champion." He waved his mallet toward the crowd around the ring. "How much am I bid for this fine animal?" He let his eyes sweep over the assembled men.

Almost half of those present were Amish farmers, weathered men wearing identical black hats, identical clothing, and beards. Their talk was simple, almost quaint, as they nodded and spoke a few brief words to each other. The auctioneer's gaze moved quickly over the Amish men. They knew horseflesh, but they wanted no part of a show animal; they bought horses for their ability to pull a plow or a wagon or one of the small, boxlike, enclosed buggies they drove when they came to town. It was a sin among them to own anything for show. Not a man among them owned a car or a tractor or a truck. Many of them turned their backs upon the chestnut and started talking to a neighbor.

"Thee plan to buy?"

Some nodded at this question; others shook their heads. There was always an economy of words in any Amish conversation.

The auctioneer finally found the face of a man he thought might be interested. The man was big, with a square, hard face. A cloth cap with ear flaps was pushed back from a high forehead. The man was staring intently at the chestnut gelding. His lips pulled into a thin line as the gelding laid back his ears and bared his teeth, then lifted both fore feet and lashed out savagely. His rider sawed hard on the broken bit, jerking the chestnut's head around. The big man nodded his head slowly. Here was a challenge, a horse that would fight back at a man. It would give him satisfaction to smash the spirit of such a horse, to break him to his will. His lips moved.

"One hundred."

A small, round man stood close to the bidder. He had been watching the face of the big man as he looked at the horse. He squeezed his bulbous nose between a thumb and forefinger, then lowered the hand to his chin.

"Two hundred," he said almost thoughtfully. He didn't plan to buy the sorrel; all he wanted to do was needle the big man. He had sized up the man and didn't like him. Here was a man who would abuse a spirited horse, and the small man loved horses.

The big man half turned and stared at the small man challengingly. The little man's eyes twinkled. The big man set his jaw into a jutting line and moved his gaze to the gelding. The chestnut tried to get his head down; he humped his back and juggled sidewise. The groom put weight on the heavy bit. The big bidder's lips moved.

"Three hundred," he said, raising his voice. Then he swiveled his head quickly and stared at the little man.

The pudgy man smiled, but he did not look at his rival. He appeared to be studying the horse carefully. He was wondering if the big man's eagerness to conquer this horse would make him go another hundred. He made up his mind and called out.

"Four hundred."

Even the Amish farmers were taking an interest in the duel between the two bidders. There seemed to be something personal in their attitudes toward each other. Perhaps they were enemies.

The big man clenched his fists; anger colored his cheeks with a deep flush. "Four fifty!" he shouted.

The little man sighed, shrugged his shoulders, and turned

away, smiling to himself, thinking that somebody should thank him for forcing the price of the chestnut outlaw up to four hundred and fifty dollars. Without competition the big man would have bought the horse for a hundred dollars. The auctioneer was happy; his commission would be four times as much as it would have been if the little man hadn't bid.

"Sold to the man wearing the black cap for four hundred fifty dollars." The auctioneer's hammer banged down on the table.

The chestnut's rider showed clearly that he was glad the bidding was over and he'd soon be off the gelding's back. He guided the prancing horse out of the ring. The Amish men gave the horse plenty of room, backing away, looking at the tall chestnut with expressionless faces. Horse fanciers in the crowd shook their heads. In their opinion the big man had made a bad bargain. The buyer shouldered his way through the crowd to the clerk's table, his checkbook in his hand, a dark scowl on his face. The thought had come to him that the little man probably hadn't intended buying the horse; he was probably a friend of the owner, a plant to push the price up.

The next horse brought in was a solid bay mare with good shoulders and legs. The harness blemishes on her shoulders indicated she had done some heavy pulling in her past. She walked into the ring and stood still, her head half lowered, her ears cocked forward. She gave the impression of being a solid work animal. At once the Amish men were attentive. Here was a work and brood horse. She could do her share of plowing and drop one colt a year. An Amish farmer turned to a friend.

"Six years."

"Thee wrong. Five," the friend said.

Now the auctioneer was watching the Amish men. There would be no cutthroat bidding among them. It would all depend upon how badly one of them needed a horse. He let them take their time looking and finally called out.

"What am I bid for this young mare?" He knew there was

no need to point out the mare's qualities to these men. Now it was the buyers who had come looking for riding or show horses who turned away and lighted cigarettes or started talking. They would have been ashamed to have this farm horse on the trails or bridle paths.

A young Amish farmer raised his voice. "Fifty dollars."

His bid was received in silence by his neighbors.

"I have fifty; who'll make it a hundred?" The auctioneer spoke impatiently. He suspected a conspiracy. The Amish people stuck together.

"Sixty." The bid came from a weather-beaten farmer whose black hat had a patched crown.

"Seventy-five," the young farmer called out.

There was no hurrying the Amish farmers. The bidding went on, and the young farmer finally bought the mare for one hundred five dollars. He could not have gone another five dollars higher, which was something most of the farmers knew and the rest guessed. The price was a bargain, and the young farmer almost smiled. He didn't because that would be showing pride. The inborn thrift of the farmers had made them push the price up a little.

One by one, the work horses and the riding stock and the ponies were bid in and taken away by their new owners. A sorry-looking black gelding was led in. His coat was coarse and dirty; he stumbled a little, favoring a foreleg. The auctioneer knew the rest of his job would be easy. The men glanced at the old horse and knew the bidding was over. They started for the several exits. Here was the first of the "killers," worn-out work animals no one would bid on except a meat dealer from a canning plant. He had four more of them to sell and, as the crowd started moving out, he called to a handler.

"Bring the rest in."

Four other horses were led into the ring, which was now deserted by all but one buyer. The last horse to walk in was a gray gelding. Ahead of him plodded three broken-down work horses, one with a sway back, another with a badly galled shoulder. The gray was chunky, though not as big as the others. His ribs were clearly outlined, his coat matted with manure and dirt; there were sores on his legs. The only proud things about him were the forward pitch of his short ears and the brightness of his eyes.

The auctioneer hardly glanced at the five horses. He looked at the lone man wearing a heavy Mackinaw coat and a cloth cap with ear flaps pulled down. The man was chewing on the stump of a cigar. He shifted it to the side of his mouth and spat upon the ground.

"Sixty a head," he said. That was the standard price for meat animals. A canner could turn a horse into profit at that price, a little for the hide, more for the meat and bones when ground and processed.

"Sold." The auctioneer didn't even pick up his mallet. He gathered up some paper, nodded to the clerk, and left the ring.

The meat buyer paid for the horses. He had hardly glanced at them as they were led out of the ring. He had no feeling at all about them. He bought killers every day. If anyone had asked him he would have told them that he was doing the old plugs a favor. Anyway, the country's millions of dogs and cats had to eat. His boss had to get horse meat at a price in order to meet competition.

The gray gelding was last out of the ring. He walked carefully and without protest, but his ears held their spirited pitch. He had had quite a few owners during the past few years. His beginning was lost in the lives of many mares and stallions. His father, perhaps a traveling stallion whose owner called at many farms, his mother a mare born to harness, with long furrows stretching before her during spring plowing, doing her share at pulling a harvester or a wagon. Now he was off to another home. He thought that because it had happened before, except that before he had been bid on or the subject of much haggling over price. Those other buyers had wanted him as a desirable work horse.

Outside the auction shed stood a big truck with its loading ramp down. The gray gelding stood waiting to be loaded, his head lowered a little. The handlers slapped the rumps of the battered horses. They shoved and growled unkind remarks as the worn-out beasts stumbled over the cleats on the ramp. The gray gelding stumbled, too, as he climbed into the truck, but, when he was shoved in beside the sway-backed black, he swung his head over the sideboard and shook it.

"That old plug has a little life left in him," one of the handlers said.

"The canners'll probably make steak out of him," another handler said and laughed.

The ramp was raised and locked into place. The meat buyer checked the lock. He was alone and wanted no trouble on his way to the slaughter pens. He turned to walk around to the cab, but paused as a station wagon pulled up beside his outfit. A man got out of the station wagon.

Because of snow squalls and a bit of tire trouble, Harry de Leyer had missed the auction. He had driven over from St. James, Long Island, hoping to add a riding horse to his stable at The Knox School for girls. Harry de Leyer is a young man, compact but not big or tall. He is blond and blue-eyed, and there is an aura of friendliness about him, a hint of dry humor. He looked at the truck, and his blue eyes swiftly checked the horses in it. Harry always pauses and looks when there are horses about. Horses are his business.

Some of the warm brightness faded from his eyes as he read the sign on the truck. It saddened him to see any horse, no matter how useless, sent to such a fate. He remembered the green pastures and fields of his Dutch homeland. Perhaps they now had dog-food factories, but they hadn't had them when he was a boy in Holland. Any horse, in Harry's opinion, deserved to end his days in a green pasture. A horse that had served a man faithfully all of his life had earned that right, the same as an ancient tiller of the soil earned the right to end his days drowsing in the sun and eating when he felt hungry.

He stepped close to the truck. Only one of the horses was paying any attention to what was going on; that was the gray gelding. The others, Harry could see, were through, no longer interested in life, breathing the cold air and letting it plume out through their nostrils in trickles of white fog. The gray gelding was just as beat up and dirty as the others. Harry looked at the head extended over the sideboards and frowned. Then he realized that it was the ears and eyes that had held his attention. It couldn't be possible, but this crossbred farm horse did have ears that reminded him of fine Arabian stock. He started to turn away, then halted. The meat buyer grinned at him. He was amused over Harry's interest in the killers. Without giving the matter much thought, Harry said, "I'd like to look that gray horse over." He nodded his head toward the gray gelding.

The meat buyer laughed. "You crazy? He's just a beat-up farm horse." But he was interested. He might get five dollars more than he had paid for the plug, which would be personal profit to him.

"Mind getting him down so I can have a look?" Harry persisted.

The buyer unfastened the ramp and dropped it. Harry reached in and caught the gray's mane. The big horse turned his head and took a step down the ramp. He stumbled and slid the rest of the way. Harry loosened his grip on the mane and stepped back. There wasn't any danger of the battered horse running away. Harry looked the gray over. He certainly wasn't much but he might do as a horse some of the heavier girls could ride. He stepped close and turned the gray around.

"How much do you want for him?" Harry asked abruptly.

The buyer considered. He was sure every horse owner knew

what was paid for killers at a sale. He was about to ask for sixty-five dollars, when Harry said, "I'll give you eighty dollars, ten for profit and ten for delivering him to my Hollandia Farm near St. James."

"You've bought yourself a horse, mister." The buyer grinned broadly. Then he took a good look at the gray and at the young man standing beside him. His conclusion was that this young man didn't know much about horses. Harry ignored the buyer; he was smiling at the gray gelding, thinking that he had probably made a bad bargain, something which seldom happened to him where horses were concerned. He caught the gray's mane and headed him back up the ramp.

The buyer lifted the ramp and locked it into place. Harry handed over eighty dollars and they shook hands, just as though this were a first-class deal.

Harry drove off, shaking his head. The truck rolled down the road after him, and the gray gelding kept his head out over the sideboards letting the wind-driven sleet pepper his face.

2 | Snowman

HARRY DE LEYER arrived at home before the gray gelding was delivered. His place was small, five and a half acres, but he owned it. He had worked hard to build up Hollandia Farm, named for his homeland. In some ways Long Island was like the countryside around St. Oedenrode, Holland, where he had grown up. Both were farming communities, and the people living in both places were horse-conscious. St. Oedenrode lacked the trees which are found on Long Island, but farming is farming everywhere, and farmers are farmers no matter where you find them. They grow about the same things in about the same way. There are fewer acres of land to a family in Holland, so much less land that young people have to wait a long time before they can hope to have enough to support a family.

And there had been a difference in horse owning when Harry was young, though there was also a similarity. The similarity was that both Long Islanders and the Dutch like horse shows. The difference was that a good show horse in Holland was supposed to earn his hay and oats working on a farm as well as parading and jumping in a show. Harry's father had insisted that the first thoroughbred Harry ever owned had to pull a plow alongside the other horses, or haul a wagon.

Harry's family met him at the door. There was at that time, Johanna, his blonde, blue-eyed wife, his son Joseph, called Chef, his daughter Harriet, and another son, Martin, known as Marty. The children ranged in ages from three to six, with Chef the eldest, then Harriet, then Marty. They were all horse lovers, including Johanna. Chef and Harriet already had their own ponies and rode them well. Harry had started riding at the age of four and saw nothing wrong with a youngster's riding as soon as he or she could climb upon the back of a horse. Harry was greeted by an eager barrage of questions. Getting a new horse was an event.

"Did you buy a horse?" they asked in unison.

Harry pushed them back into the kitchen. "I was late getting to the auction, but I bought a horse." Harry was beginning to worry a little about what they would think when they saw the gray gelding. The De Leyer horses were matters of family pride. Wasn't Harry riding master at the exclusive Knox School for girls? A De Leyer horse had to have class because the daughters of wealthy people rode them.

"When's he coming?" Chef asked. Three small, blond heads bobbed, and three pairs of blue eyes looked up into Harry's face.

"I get to ride him first," Harriet chipped in. It was best to be fast when Chef was around.

"He needs some training," Harry said cautiously.

"What's he look like?" Chef asked.

"A little over sixteen hands high, I'd say." Then he added quickly, "He has a fine head, Arabian ears, mighty lively eyes."

"What did you pay for him?" the thrifty Johanna asked.

Harry grinned at his wife. She is a small, pert girl, pretty and not much changed from the girl Harry married just before leaving Holland.

"Eighty dollars," he said.

"Eighty bucks." Chef snorted. Harry and Johanna still talk with a Dutch accent, but not their offspring. They talk like any American youngster who sees American TV and reads American books and has American friends.

"Sounds like some old farm nag," Harriet said.

"It's up to you and Chef to help train him. We have to make a riding horse out of him or we can't keep him." Harry was thinking of the meat buyer as he spoke.

The discussion was halted by the sound of a truck pulling into the yard. Chef and Harriet dashed out through the kitchen door with Marty close upon their heels. Johanna and Harry followed them out into the yard. Harry's stubborn streak was stirring. He'd make a riding horse out of the gray nag just as he had made a success out of a good many things since coming to America.

Snow was falling, big flakes which floated down gently in a white mass. The truck driver was already out of his cab. He was in a hurry because of the storm. If a wind sprang up, the snowfall could turn into a blizzard. Harry helped the buyer lower the ramp, and together they guided the gelding out of the truck. He stumbled clumsily down the ramp and stood looking at his new family. Harry was glad he was coated with a blanket of white snow. He raised his head, with his ears cocked forward.

"A snowman!" Chef and Harriet shouted.

"What a wonderful name for him." Johanna turned to Harry. "If he does not have a name."

"No name," Harry answered.

"Snowman, Snowman," the children chorused, with Marty joining in.

That settled the matter of a name. The gelding was Snowman from then on. Harry turned to Chef. "Run and get a halter."

Chef darted away. The buyer slapped snow from his gloves. "He's all yours," he said. "I'll be on my way." He hurried to his truck and climbed in.

Snowman shook himself but didn't get rid of much snow. Chef came dashing back with a halter, and Harry slipped it on the gray's head. Chef raised a hand and slid it over Snowman's shoulder. It came away black and grimy. It also revealed the sad condition of the horse's coat. Chef looked at his grimy hand and scowled. Snowman lowered his head toward Chef. Chef turned to his father, his eyes big.

"He winked at me," he said solemnly.

Harry de Leyer laughed. Oddly enough, he had got the impression back at the auction yard that the big gray had winked at him. But he wasn't admitting it. "Probably a snowflake in his eye," he said, but he shook his head.

Later other people got that impression, probably because Snowman had a way of turning his head, just as though about to make a funny observation, much as a person might do.

Harriet moved in close to Chef and rubbed a patch of snow off the other shoulder. "We'll make a fine horse out of you," she said softly.

Unnoticed, Marty slipped past Chef and wrapped his small arms around one of Snowman's forelegs, squealing with delight. Snowman lowered his muzzle and nudged the little boy. Harry moved in fast, but there was nothing to fear. Johanna caught Marty by an arm and held him away from her.

"Look at you," she scolded. "You're covered with nasty dirt. I'll have to change your clothes."

They all looked at Marty and laughed. He even had a smudge of smelly dirt on one cheek, but he wasn't unhappy. He rubbed the smudge with a chubby fist. "Snowman," he said and tried to pull away from his mother.

Johanna, with Harriet and Marty, went into the house out of the storm. Harry and Chef led Snowman to the stable. As they moved along, Harry's head was full of plans for training the gray gelding. There are many ways of training a horse. Some men, like the man who bought the unruly chestnut at the New Holland auction, set out to break the horse's spirit and will, to rule by fear. Other men lavish care on a horse, but control him with a firm hand. The last is the way Harry de Leyer trains a horse. He can be firm and tough, but he aims to win the trust and affection of a horse if he can. Naturally that is the approach used by all of the De Leyer clan.

The first step was to make Snowman look like a horse. This was a family project. They all donned wooden shoes, sent to them from Holland and worn when working around the stable. The shoes were kept outside the kitchen door and removed before entering the house. They washed Snowman as many times as was necessary to get the dirt and slime out of his coat and off his skin. They clipped him slightly and combed and brushed him. Harry called in his horseshoer and had him shod. Chef and Harriet did the currying and combing. They worked at it until all of the loose, dead hair was gone and his coat began to shine. The sores on his legs were doctored carefully. But no amount of grooming could remove the marks left by the heavy work harness he had once worn. Those marks would always be visible to anyone who looked closely.

It took time to get all of this accomplished, and during the process Snowman began to change enough so that they could all notice it. He was as calm and unruffled as ever, and his temper remained even, but he began showing signs of being alive and liking it. Grain and clean hay made him fill out. His neck arched more, and his ribs did not stand out so prominently. He was like a tramp who has had a chance to clean up and put on good

clothes. Looking him over, Harry said to Johanna, "He'll be able to carry some of the heavier girls at the school."

"I think Chef and Harriet have plans for keeping him here at Hollandia," Johanna answered with a smile. "They are very fond of him, and Marty likes him."

"I'm in the horse business," Harry reminded her. "Here at Hollandia no one would rent and ride a plow horse. But at the school they will. Remember how father always said that every horse we owned had to earn his feed."

Johanna nodded. They stood and watched Chef and Harriet work on Snowman, Harriet on one side with a brush, Chef on the other with a curry comb. Harry laughed.

"I wish I could get them as interested in the station wagon. It needs washing and polishing."

"Seems like I remember how you acted when you were their age," Johanna said. "Didn't you ride a winner at the fair when you were nine?"

Harry smiled. "I would have washed father's new truck if the Germans hadn't grabbed it a few weeks after he bought it. We were all very proud of that new Ford truck." He stirred himself and moved toward Snowman. "Guess I'll start working him before Harriet and Chef wear him out with their brushing and combing."

At that moment Marty came rushing out of the tack room. He had hay in his hair and he was dragging a bridle he had found in the tack room.

"Wanna ride," he shouted as he ran toward Snowman, waving the bridle.

"Put that bridle back where you got it," Harry ordered sternly. "After we teach Snowman a few things you can ride him."

Marty halted and looked up at his father defiantly. He knew he was going to obey, but he had to make a show of resistance. He swung the bridle back and forth a few times and muttered,

"Wanna ride." Then he turned and trudged away to the tack room.

The first thing a plow horse has to learn, if he is to become a reliable riding horse, is sure-footedness over obstacles which might be found on a trail or on a cross-country trip. Harry and Chef laid a network of thick poles on the ground, placing them several feet apart. The trick, in walking over the poles, was to make the horse learn to lift his feet high and space his steps right. Harry led Snowman over the course in a trial walk. Harriet and Chef were upset over the result. Poles flipped and were scattered about as Snowman ambled over them clumsily, paying no attention to them at all. Chef and Harriet rearranged the poles and sat down to watch a second trial. Harry smiled as he headed the big gray back over the poles.

The second time over, Snowman began to understand that a flipped pole could hurt when it rapped his legs. But he scattered a lot of poles and brought an anguished wail from Harriet.

"He's so clumsy he'll throw off the girls." She jumped to her feet and shook a finger at the big gray. "Pick up your feet, clumsy."

"Just think what would happen if he started to run," Chef said and laughed.

"Straighten out the poles," Harry ordered.

Chef and Harriet arranged the poles again. They kept at the training until Snowman began to lift his feet and space his steps. After a while he was able to trot over the poles and then he was sent over them at a lope. Finally he was able to gallop along and never hit a pole.

It was then that Marty got to ride Snowman. A saddle had been picked for the gray, and he had been taught the feel of it with a person on his back. Harry rode him first to make certain he would not resent the saddle and try to fight it. Then Harriet rode him and Chef. He took it all in stride, and Chef was able to gallop him around the paddock. When Marty was hoisted into the saddle, Snowman walked sedately around the paddock, even though Marty did pepper away with his small heels and shout in an effort to get Snowman to run.

The big gray gelding was more interested in people than he was in other horses. He mingled with the riding stock and the hunters and jumpers but liked to do his frolicking by himself.

He wasn't exactly a show-off; he was placid and deliberate most of the time. He didn't have to be urged to run; he seemed to enjoy it, and he wasn't apt to burst into the wild action which sometimes took hold of the thoroughbreds. Watching him one morning, Harry remarked to Johanna, "Once a plow horse, always a plow horse."

"You know better than that," Johanna answered. "Remember those two plow horses on the tobacco farm?"

Harry nodded. He certainly remembered that tobacco farm where he had started life in America as a sharecropper. He was supposed to split the profits fifty-fifty with the owner. It looked like a wonderful opportunity for them in the new world, a big farm which made the little Dutch farms back home look like garden plots. Fine, black soil that could grow anything.

It had been a rosy beginning. Coming over steerage on the Dutch flagship, *Westerforn*, had been their honeymoon. There had been long happy days aboard. They had saved one hundred and eighty dollars, which was all they were allowed to take out of Holland. It wasn't much, but it seemed to them to be pretty good capital, and their Dutch thrift had kept them from wasting any of it on luxuries. When they docked they refused to tip the steerage steward twenty dollars, instead offering him the Dutch equivalent of five dollars, which seemed to them to be a very generous sum. Even the captain wasn't able to convince Harry that he should part with twenty dollars to a man who was being paid to do a job.

Harry had worked so hard on that farm, chopping weeds out of the tobacco rows and driving a cultivator, that he dropped in weight from one hundred and sixty pounds to one hundred and twenty-eight. They lived in a sharecropper's shack, but it was like a palace because they had love and would soon have money from their share of the crop. Johanna fixed the house up, made curtains, and stuffed cushions. Harry added a touch of paint to the furniture. And there had been the two plow horses, old and heavy. Harry had worked on them and had trained one of them to jump a little. He had even won ten dollars at a local village horse show. The owner frowned upon such foolishness, but Harry was such a hard worker that he did not argue much about the spare-time training of the horses.

A lot of that summer had been good. There had been a few really wonderful times, like the day Johanna was sure they were going to have a baby. But when harvest time came the tobacco crop was a complete failure. Harry got fifty per cent of nothing, and their capital had been used up for living expenses. They had to start all over again—this time broke. The owner of the farm couldn't advance them any money to carry them through another year. Yes, Harry remembered that tobacco farm and the two old horses. He smiled as he watched Snowman galloping around the paddock, taking it easy but covering a lot of ground. The big gray was certainly developing a powerful set of leg muscles. He would be a riding horse who would not tire easily, a fine animal on the steep hill trails.

"I'm glad I listened to those American paratroopers when they told me stories about America," he said with a smile.

After the tobacco-farm venture he had begun to wonder. Now he was glad he had listened to Larry and the older Nelson and the dark-faced boy they called Pierre, because he looked French or Spanish. They had all extolled the wonders of America. They had been American boys, homesick for a town or village they had left behind to fight a war on foreign soil. Larry had talked about a big farm somewhere in the vast midsection of the United States. Harry couldn't remember the town or the state, but he did remember how Larry had described the endless rows of tall corn, the wide pastures with their herds of cattle.

He had liked Larry best, but when Pierre and Nelson came to visit at the De Leyer home later, while on leave, Larry was not with them and they did not want to talk about him, and Harry guessed that he had been killed in action. He was never to know, but he guessed it had happened not far from St. Oedenrode.

America and its people had been good to the De Leyers. He even harbored no ill feeling toward the tobacco farmer. But everything went back to, and was tied in with, things that had happened in Holland. There was the grave of Mickey Shultz, who had died while floating down in his parachute just outside the village. Johanna's family, the Vermeltfoorts, had cared for the grave, even though they had never met Mickey. Mickey's mother had been grateful. She had visited the grave and met the Vermeltfoort family and visited with them. When Johanna's sister, Walda, decided she wanted to come to America, Mrs. Shultz had sponsored her and made her entry possible. And that had led to the sponsorship of Johanna and Harry. Without such slender threads they could never have come.

As Harry returned Snowman to his stall he went on remembering. As a boy of sixteen, he had helped the underground hide and feed prominent citizens who were marked by the Nazis for concentration, or labor, camps. Harry's father was a prominent citizen and community leader so that he was on their wanted list. He operated a brewery as well as a farm. Harry and others watched for strange trucks or cars on the country roads and warned of their approach so that the hunted men could take cover. Every farm family watched for strangers so that catching the fugitives was a hard job for the Germans.

Being only a boy, Harry did not attract the attention of the Nazi soldiers and police who came to collect produce and stock and to search for those on their wanted list. When the paratroopers came, Harry and the other village boys were on hand to watch. Nothing the Nazi soldiers could do kept the boys from being almost in the middle of the battle. It was exciting watching the parachutes float down and seeing how the invaders dug in quickly and expertly. Bullets flew but none of the boys got hit. They were, in fact, a cheering section for the invading Yanks.

He remembered how he really got into action when tracer bullets set fire to the thatched roof of a hospital which housed old people as well as bed patients. The hospital was between the Nazi and Yank lines of fire. The soldiers were too busy shooting at each other to put out the fire. In order to get at it, someone had to drag a fire hose along a low wall. Harry was the only available male big enough to drag the hose. He volunteered for the job, and, while his father stood at the hydrant waiting to turn on the water, Harry crawled along the wall and got the hose in place. The stream of water put out the fire, but not before a number of Yanks had come to help Harry. That was how he met Larry, Nelson, and Pierre. For a time he stayed with the paratroopers and helped them. When the fighting slackened, they visited at his home.

After the fire there had been a village celebration at which Harry received a citation for what he had done. But the best part of the adventure had been getting to know the three Americans.

Now Harry had a boarding and rental stable at Hollandia Farm and a good job as riding instructor at The Knox School. He had some show horses that had won ribbons. He had much to be thankful for and he admitted it as he patted Snowman's gray shoulder. The big gelding had brought back a lot of memories. He was like no other horse Harry had ever owned. There was nothing distinguished about him. He was just a plow horse that had learned to carry a rider, but he had roused in Harry de Leyer a strong attachment.

3 | The Knox School

THE KNOX SCHOOL for girls has a tradition of fifty-seven industrious years behind it. Thousands of girls have received an important part of their education in its beautiful surroundings. It stands amid rolling, wooded hills, with its own beach and with meadows and thickets which, in the spring, are aflame with dogwood blossoms. Only large estates are allowed in this area. There are no commercial enterprises or small businesses. There are miles of wild wooded country to ride through. It is, of course, a very select school with high tuition rates. Girls trained by Harry de Leyer have ridden in many junior shows as well as in the National Show at Madison Square Garden in New York. Most of the girls can afford to own thoroughbred horses, and many of them do. These horses are boarded by Harry at the school stables. If they are show horses, Harry trains them for the girls.

Into this elite company came Snowman. He was not awed or impressed by the group of spirited thoroughbreds he mingled with in the paddock or on the group rides into the hills. He swung along with the high-steppers and came in after a long ride much fresher than they.

Snowman was just right for the timid, sometimes awkward, girls who were afraid of more spirited mounts. They felt secure and could even show off a little while riding him. He eased Harry's worry over an inept rider being thrown. A girl who was self-conscious about her weight and a bit clumsy found Snowman just the horse for her. He gave them confidence as well as a smooth, easy ride—no jolting or jiggling, no shying when a rabbit broke cover along the trail or a fox flashed out from underfoot. A few of the girls started asking for him.

Chef and Harriet were deeply disappointed when the big gray left Hollandia Farm to live at the school. But they had other horses and soon ceased missing him. Harry began thinking about what he would do with the extra riding horses when the summer season was over. He was in the horse business to make money; an idle horse cost him for grain and feed. There was no reason for keeping over an ordinary riding horse like Snowman who could easily be replaced. He was not like the spirited show horses Harry often bought cheap because they had been ruined by bad handling. Those he kept, knowing that, after he had cured them of their bad habits, he could sell them at a good profit. He had made Snowman into a horse that would sell for perhaps double what Harry had paid for him, though he wasn't a show horse. He was aware that most people, looking for a riding horse, might not want such a placid and un-showy an animal. Of course, the gelding could not be sold as a farm work horse. The Amish farmers would certainly bid on him, but they weren't apt to go as high as a hundred and sixty dollars.

Harry de Leyer shouldn't have had any great interest in the

gray gelding. He wasn't a hunter or a jumper, and those were the types of horses Harry specialized in. He had made a winner out of Sinjon, a horse whose owner had discarded him because no trainer or rider seemed able to handle him safely. Sinjon had proved himself notoriously unreliable on a tough course before Harry got him. He could jump and he had class, but no one wanted to take him over the jumps and risk a bad fall or be shown up by a horse who refused a barrier and bolted off course. Harry took him, rode him, and made a winner out of him. Sinjon wound up as a valuable member of the U. S. Equestrian Team.

There was Wayward Wind, a fine little mare who had a bad fall which resulted in twenty-one stitches being taken in her chest. Her jumping days were over, said the horse experts; she'd never try another barrier. Harry got her as a discard and made a champion out of her. Wayward Wind was just coming on at the time Harry was considering selling Snowman. But she was worth a dozen horses like the gray gelding. Harry had big plans in store for Wayward Wind.

But there was sentiment. The gray gelding was the sort of horse a man got attached to the way a man gets attached to a fine collie. Toward the end of the summer, Harry began to hope one of the big girls who rode and liked Snowman would want to buy him. If one of the girls bought him he would be stabled at the school at least during the summer. He watched the girls who rode the big gray. Any of them could afford to pay a hundred and sixty dollars for a horse. They all liked him, but none of them ever spoke of wanting to buy him, even though Harry hinted about it.

Harry thought things over and decided he knew why none of the girls ever thought of buying the horse. None of them had developed a personal attachment for any horse. Their minds were occupied by other things. A girl needed to learn to ride gracefully; it was a part of her social training at Knox. It was the thing you should do, and it fitted her for the sort of life she would lead later. Harry got to comparing these girls with Johanna as he had known her as a teen-ager back in Holland. He had a feeling these girls had missed many of the good things Johanna had experienced.

Johanna had attended a girls' school in Holland. There were no schools where boys and girls attended the same classes. But she had lived at home. She and Harry had been part of the community life. On Sunday there had been church services attended by everyone. Necessary tasks were quickly finished, and each person got into his or her best clothes and went to mass. Afterward there might be bicycle rides or strolls or just lazing in the shade. The day always had a strong religious flavor, but there was much enjoyment and much mingling after girls and boys grew up enough to notice each other.

And there were always community affairs, the visiting Russian riders, horsemen who did thrilling trick riding and saber drills. Everyone went to see the Russians because everyone liked horses. There had been the traveling circus which made the twelve De Leyer children—seven boys and five girls—clamor for small change so that they could see everything. In that brood Harry was the eldest. He and Johanna had attended the horse shows and the circus together as soon as they were old enough to have a feeling for each other. But it had always been the horses, even at the circus, which attracted them most. Wild animals, yes, but they mostly just sat and looked out of cages, yawning their boredom. Of course there were the lion and tiger and bear acts, but they did not compare to the flash and color and beauty of the barebacked riders and their horses.

Then Harry had started riding in junior shows and Johanna sat in the stands, just as she does now while Harry is riding a jumper. No, the Knox girls didn't have what Johanna had known.

He doubted if any of them had ever been to a carnival like the one he and Johanna had attended—the many side shows and the portable dance floor housed in a huge tent, the music boxes grinding out tunes. He had a feeling the Knox girls didn't go to mixed community dances in a village. They danced together and went to formals, but they missed the fun of mingling with all sorts of youngsters.

Long before the summer was over Harry gave up hoping one of his girls would buy Snowman. He'd have to find a buyer or take the gray back to the New Holland auction where he had found him.

Snowman returned to Hollandia Farm and seemed happy to be back. He at once became an item in the account book which showed a loss. Harry looked around for a buyer, but no one seemed to want a reliable plow horse who was also a safe, if not exciting, mount. The difficulty was to find some person who wanted such a horse. Finally Harry made up his mind. He'd take Snowman in to New Holland on a Monday. The big gray was no longer in danger of being sold for meat. He was sure an Amish farmer would buy him and treat him well. There would be no big profit but there would be some, and his Dutch thrift made him determined to sell for more than he had paid.

But Harry never loaded Snowman up and hauled him to the auction. One day a neighbor—a doctor—stopped by, looking for a riding horse. The doctor had an office in town and a small place several miles from Hollandia Farm. The De Leyer family seldom needed a doctor, except when the children had been born, so Harry did not know the man personally. The doctor got out of his car and looked the paddock and stable over. His knowledge of such things was limited. Harry came out of the tack room and greeted his visitor.

"You are looking for a horse?" Harry smiled and added, "That's all we have here at Hollandia Farm."

"Yes. I want a safe horse, one that I don't have to worry about when my boy goes riding. I don't want an animal that prances around. From what I have observed, all riding horses prance and are flighty." The doctor shook his head. "I may want to take a ride at times myself." He looked at Harry questioningly. "I don't suppose you have such a horse for sale?"

Harry's face broke into a broad smile. "I have just the horse you want," he said.

"I'll look at him," the doctor said cautiously. "But he must be guaranteed gentle."

"I'll guarantee him," Harry said. The doctor seemed a pleasant sort, not a man who would abuse a horse. Harry felt he was very lucky.

They went into the paddock, and Harry led Snowman out of the stable and turned him loose. Snowman trotted about with his head up. His gait was easy, and he didn't appear concerned about anything. He did give the doctor a look or two but he always did that when people were looking at him. He came to Harry at once when Harry whistled to him and thrust out his head to be scratched. Harry didn't scratch his neck, because, when he did, Snowman always rolled up his upper lip and bared his teeth in a grimace which might have made the doctor uneasy. Harry just patted the broad muzzle.

"He's a fine family horse," Harry said.

"Pretty big animal, but he looks safe enough," the doctor said. Being a doctor and not a horse expert or fancier, he was interested mostly in Snowman's amiable temperament. "How much do you want for him?" Again he was cautious. He had been warned by friends that a good saddle horse cost quite a bit of money.

"One hundred and sixty dollars," Harry answered promptly. He looked affectionately at the big gray and felt a pang of regret over the thought of parting with him. He half hoped the doctor would balk at the price. His feelings prompted him to add, "But if you ever sell him it must be to me. I'll pay you what you pay me for him."

The doctor smiled eagerly. Here was a real guarantee, his money back if he didn't like the horse and wanted to get rid of him. "It's a deal." The doctor got his checkbook out of his pocket and fished for his pen.

Harry returned Snowman to his stall and made out a bill of sale. They exchanged pieces of paper and shook hands.

"I'll run him over later," Harry promised.

"There is no great hurry," the doctor assured him. "I've been standing the boy off for a month. A little more delay won't matter."

The doctor got into his car and drove out of the yard.

The doctor's car was hardly out of the yard before the family converged on Harry to say good-by to Snowman. The big gray gelding had made a place for himself in the hearts of each. Harry went into the stable and led Snowman out. He might as well get the parting over with. As always, Snowman enjoyed having the family make a fuss over him. He stamped a hoof and jerked at the lead rope, asking to be turned loose so he could show off. Harry jerked the rope and said gruffly, "No run today. You're going for a ride."

"Is that doctor a nice man?" Harriet asked anxiously.

"He is a very nice man. His son will be good to Snowman," Harry assured her.

"He knows how to take care of a horse?" Johanna asked with a small frown.

Harry hesitated. He had been so eager to have the big gray find an owner like the doctor that he hadn't questioned him as to how much he knew about taking care of a horse. "He has enough pasture and a barn for winter shelter," he said. "I'll tell the boy about grain and grooming."

Little Marty interrupted the talk. He had slipped around behind Snowman. He reached up and gripped the flowing tail.
Snowman looked around, but he didn't move until Harry had
gathered Marty up and set him beside his mother.

"Never do that again," he said sharply. "Other horses will
kick."

"I guess we'll see him some," Chef said. "I'll ride over there
once in a while."

"A good idea," Harry said. He himself wanted to keep in
touch with the big gray.

Johanna and Harriet gave the big horse a hug. Chef stood
back, refusing to show how he felt. Marty clamored to be put on
Snowman's back. Harry swung him up and then led the gray
gelding to the trailer hitched back of the pickup truck. Harry
swung Marty down, and the family stood close to the trailer
while Snowman was being loaded. He went up eagerly enough.
There had been little excitement for him since his return to
the farm. Harry got in back of the wheel. Starting the engine,
he pulled swiftly out of the yard.

A misty-eyed family watched the gray rump and tail vanish
down the driveway. That is the way with the De Leyer clan.
They have had a stable of fine horses for a long time, some of
them blue-ribbon winners. But, as they stood there that day, they
were saddened over parting with an easy-going gray gelding
who had never done anything exciting or unusual except make
his personality felt. Chef spoke up.

"Won't be the same around here. That Snowman was sure
a real clown."

No one had thought of it that way before, but now that
Chef put it into words they all agreed. Snowman was a horse
with a sense of humor.

"That doctor better treat him good," Harriet said and meant
every word she said.

"Yeah," Chef said, almost to himself. "He sure did wink at me that first time."

They walked to the house, where Johanna busied herself getting ready the evening meal. Harriet and Chef were quiet for a while. Soon they were romping and playing, but they weren't forgetting Snowman.

4 | Fences Make Good Neighbors

HARRY DE LEYER entered the doctor's one hundred and sixty dollars in his ledger with satisfaction. The children were in bed, Johanna was sewing on a dress for Harriet. A tomboy like Harriet needed clothes which could stand a lot of wear and tear. Harry had put in a full day, and now he had earned an hour or so, of relaxation. After he closed the ledger he spent some time thinking, looking back—something he seldom had time to do.

The year Chef was born had been their toughest. Broke and out of a job, he had gone with Johanna to live with her sister. The baby was due to arrive in three months. The total cost in doctor and hospital bills would be one hundred and thirty-five dollars. Harry had searched everywhere for a job, any kind of a job that would bring in some money. The only job he could find was working in a dairy. There wasn't a stable job open anywhere. It looked as though his dream to work with horses was doomed to fade away. His future seemed to be with cows, and he didn't like cows.

But he dug in and took spare-time jobs to add a little extra money. He even managed to buy an ancient car which was in such a state of disrepair that Johanna had to hold a flashlight over the side when they drove at night. Harry just couldn't afford to buy parts to fix the lights.

He stuck to the cows until Chef was born. When the bills were paid, he didn't have money left to buy an airmail stamp to rush the good news to his folks in Holland. But he and Johanna were not downcast. Chef was a wonderful baby, and a week before he had arrived, Harry had received a telegram offering him a job at Brackerston, Pennsylvania. The job was with a stable, working horses. The owner of the stable, Will G. Sterling, had heard about Harry from Mickey Welch, a shrewd judge of men and horseflesh, who had seen Harry ride in an amateur show while he was working the tobacco farm. At the time Mickey had talked to Harry, he liked the young man's way with a horse—even an old plow horse turned jumper. He had advised Harry to stick with jumpers. Harry had been eager enough but had been forced to settle for black and white cows.

Mickey had told Bill Sterling, of the Stirrup Hill Horse Farm, that Harry had had quite a bit of experience with hunters and jumpers. This was true. He had started riding at the age of four and had ridden in junior shows from the age of nine on. He had been a member of the Junior Dutch Olympic Team during 1948 and 1949 and had competed in many shows in Europe. In 1949 he had placed third in the International show in Belgium. But he readily admitted he had a lot yet to learn about training horses as a business, which was what he meant to do sometime.

Bill Sterling liked the way Harry handled the jumpers. He could manage almost any horse and he was an expert rider who got top performance from a jumper. But Harry wanted to go on; he wanted to be on his own. So, after a stay on Stirrup Hill Farm, he went to work for David Hough Dillard, a wealthy horse fancier. Harry smiled as he shoved the ledger into a desk drawer. He owed a lot to chunky David Dillard, who was so short he couldn't see over the wheel of his Cadillac without craning his neck. Dillard was many times over a millionaire. Born a very poor boy, one of thirteen children, David had worked his way to the top. Coca-Cola's Six-Pack packaging was his idea, and he formed a company to manufacture the cartons. Other ventures followed, all successful. He had taught Harry sound business sense, especially how to profit from running a horse farm.

Dillard, at that time, had four show horses, all of them fine animals. Harry worked with them on the Lynchburg farm. He showed the horses and started planning on owning some of his own. His first buy set the pattern for what was to follow. He bought an unmanageable horse for twenty-five dollars and, with patient handling, got the horse over his bad habits. But his twenty-five-dollar horse didn't show much promise. It wasn't until he bought a horse named Don River that he had a real show animal. And he paid the highest price for Don River that he had ever paid for a horse, six hundred dollars, most of which he borrowed from Dillard, who knew the jumper was a bargain at the price.

Harry got up from his desk. Don River had been worth the six hundred dollars. Harry had made a profit on him, but he was the last horse Harry put so much money into. He soon learned he could make a jumper out of a horse that cost a lot less. Stepping outside the kitchen, he put on his wooden shoes and walked down to the stable for a final check. Everything was in order, and he turned back toward the house. Pausing, he looked up at the clear, star-studded sky. Now he had his own farm. He had bought and sold and trained many horses. He had a good job as riding master at The Knox School, but he wanted more. He yearned for a jumper who would be national champion—the crowning achievement of any trainer or owner. He knew he wasn't anywhere near the top. He'd probably never be wealthy enough to buy a champion. He shrugged his shoulders, knowing well that if he had the money he wouldn't buy a champion. He'd have to find the right horse, raw material out of which he could mold and shape a champion.

Sinjon had been close. Wayward Wind would be good but never the horse he dreamed about. But he'd keep on looking. Someday that horse would come into his life; he was sure of it.

Life for Snowman at the doctor's place was different from what it had been at Hollandia Farm and at the Knox School stables. It wasn't bad, but Snowman had tasted the pleasures of a real horse farm, and he missed the good care and good grooming. Being at the doctor's was like being back on the farm, except that he didn't have a lot of hard work to do. He could exercise in the pasture and he did when he got restless, and he got a measure of grain once in a while, when either the son or the doctor thought about it. But he was a horse that liked companionship, and on the little farm he was often left alone.

The son rode him, but the placid plow horse lacked the class the boy saw in other riding horses. The doctor rode him a couple of times and decided that there was little merit in horseback riding. By the time spring came, Snowman was so restless he would have welcomed the heavy farm work he used to do at spring-plowing time. He was bored and lonesome.

Long Island in the vicinity of St. James is farm and estate country—a beautiful spot with spreading fields, woods, and large residential places surrounded by shrubbery, shade trees, and clipped lawns. There are many large potato farms as well as grain and hay fields. The people are thrifty and careful, with a rich past back of them. They are proud of their farms and homes, and lavish care upon them.

One morning, as the doctor drove out of his yard, he was met by his next-door neighbor, who seemed to be highly irritated. The doctor stopped his car, thinking his professional services might be needed. The neighbor gave him a cold stare. He moved around to the driver's side of the car.

"I have something to show you," he said grimly.

"Where?" The doctor was puzzled and disturbed by his neighbor's belligerent attitude.

"At my place."

The doctor opened the far door. "Get in," he said. "I'll drive you over to your place."

The neighbor walked around the car and got in. He was a man of few words and saved them until the car stopped at his gate and he and the doctor got out. The neighbor owned a big house with spacious, landscaped grounds, the central attraction being a well-kept lawn. The whole yard was surrounded by a high stone fence with a wrought-iron gate. The neighbor nodded toward his yard.

"There," he said tersely.

They moved to the high iron gate, which the neighbor opened. After they stepped through the gate the doctor looked around, wondering what he was supposed to see. The first thing he noticed were deep imprints of a horse's hoofs on the lawn. It was clear that a big-footed horse had wandered about over the lawn, cropping grass. The doctor's gaze shifted to a flower bed. Some asters and tulips had been trampled, and the top of a budding spiraea bush had been cropped away. The doctor shook his head and looked at his neighbor.

"It would appear that you have been visited by a stray horse." He turned to look at the stone fence. "I take it that your gate was left open." This seemed a reasonable deduction because the stone wall was over four feet high and at least two feet wide at the top.

"The gate was closed and latched; it always is because it works by a spring which closes it," the neighbor said firmly.

"Impossible," the doctor commented. He was a man of science and not given to wild surmise.

"My dog awakened me this morning, and when I went to my bedroom window I saw him chasing a gray horse. That horse jumped right over my fence." The neighbor's voice rose. "My wife also saw the horse."

"A gray horse?" The doctor couldn't see how he could be connected with such vandalism.

"Your horse." The neighbor almost shouted. "We watched him run across the road and down to your pasture. He ran away from my dog and jumped over your fence."

"Impossible," muttered the bewildered doctor. "That horse couldn't jump over a log in the road. I know; I've ridden him on several occasions."

"If it happens again, I'll call the state police and the sheriff's office." The neighbor glared at the doctor.

"I'm sorry," the doctor said lamely. "De Leyer never told me that horse was a jumper. He actually guaranteed that he would not jump around or act up."

"No matter, he jumps." The neighbor turned toward his house.

"I'll pay the damages," the doctor called after the irate man.

The neighbor paused and looked back. "No damages. Just raise that fence of yours a foot or two." He stamped off into the house, slamming the door after him and leaving the doctor standing staring at big hoof prints in the lawn. Shaking his head, the doctor walked to the high gate and unlatched it. He was muttering to himself as he drove away.

The doctor drove into town and called Harry de Leyer as soon as he reached his office. He knew his neighbor was a conservative man who had been a good neighbor for a number of years. When Harry answered the phone the doctor got to the point at once.

"Is that Snowman horse you sold me a jumper?" he asked.

Harry smiled into the receiver. "No," he said promptly. "When I got him he had trouble stepping over a few poles scattered on the ground."

The doctor sighed. He was greatly relieved. "Thanks," he said.

The doctor's feeling of relief didn't last. Before seeing his first patient, he called up a handy man and made a deal with him to raise the fence a foot. He decided the best thing to do was to be on the safe side.

Several mornings later Harry de Leyer got up early as he always did. He got into his wooden shoes and started off to the stable to clean it and take care of the horses. A fresh breeze was blowing in from the nearby fields, birds sang in the trees bordering the paddock. The breeze flowed past the stable and paddock and carried the horsy smell of the stable to Harry. This was a time of the day that he thoroughly enjoyed. He stopped at the paddock gate and reached for the bar, then dropped his hand and stood staring into the enclosure.

A gray horse was frolicking around inside the paddock. Harry blinked; the horse was Snowman. Then he looked carefully at the barred gate. The bar was firmly in place. His gaze moved around the fence. Everything was as it should be; no rail was down; there wasn't a break anyplace. Harry whistled. Snowman whirled and loped over to the gate. Harry looked at him for a few moments; then he laughed.

"Well," he said, and shook his head.

Snowman nickered softly and swung his muzzle over the gate. Harry reached out and scratched the gray neck, sinking his fingers deep. Snowman curled up his upper lip in a happy grimace and bared his teeth. He was very happy to be back, and full of energy. Harry studied the powerful hind legs. It could be possible, though it was fantastic, bordering on the impossible. You had to train a horse to jump, and someone had to ride him to get him over a high jump. But one thing was certain and real.

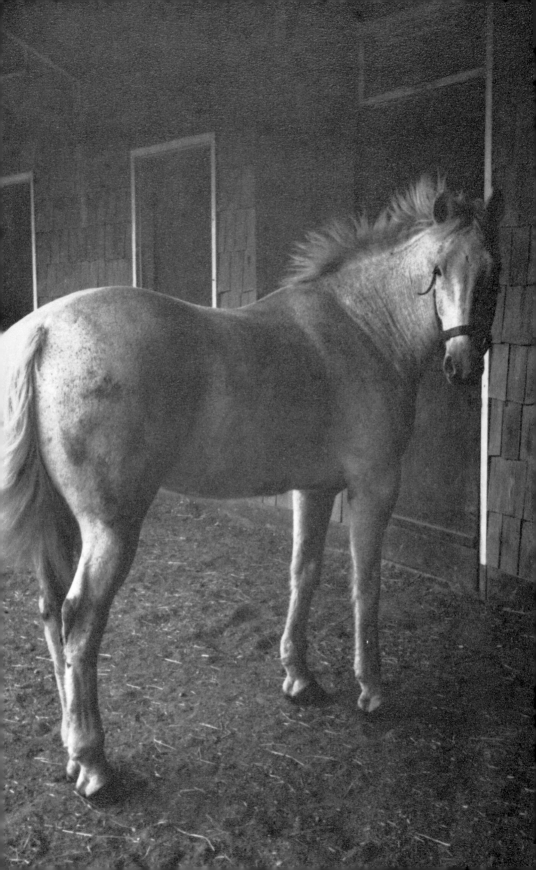

Snowman was back in the Hollandia paddock. This called for some investigating. He patted the big gray's neck.

"I'd better look into this," he said, and turned toward the house.

At the kitchen door he kicked off his wooden shoes and went through the kitchen to the living room, where he sat down beside the phone table and looked up the doctor's country number. He dialed and had only to wait a few minutes before the doctor's voice came over the wire. It ruffled with anger when Harry said, "This is De Leyer calling. I have your horse here in my paddock." He waited, and the explosion came.

"Yes, my horse is gone," the doctor snapped. "I had my pasture fence raised a foot. I've already had three calls from angry potato farmers. That horse damaged a lot of potato plants. He charged around in at least three fields. The state police are on the way out here."

Harry hesitated. "I think it must have been an accident," he said without much conviction. "I never taught that gray horse to jump. I've never even seen him jump over anything higher than a pole lying on the ground."

"It's no accident. Those farmers are threatening to sue me. I may even be arrested when the police arrive." The doctor's voice had risen to a shout.

"I guess he jumps," Harry said. "There is no other way he could get into my paddock unless you put him there."

"I haven't seen him since yesterday. I'm holding you to the bargain we made." The doctor was making an effort to calm himself. "You buy that horse back, or I'll get rid of him to the first person I meet." He sputtered a little, then added, "I don't want him back here."

Harry smiled broadly. He was glad Snowman was back. "I'll be over with a check," he said. "Tell the police and the potato farmers that there will be no more damage to their crops." He hung up and sat looking thoughtfully at the telephone.

He had worked jumping horses all of his life but he had never met one that had learned to jump by himself. He had never known of one that jumped, apparently, for fun. There was something very interesting here. He had already given up the idea that the doctor had anything to do with the big gray getting out of his pasture and into the Hollandia Farm paddock. Snowman had jumped, and he had cleared some very formidable barriers. Harry's paddock fence was designed to keep jumpers inside the yard. He was positive that he owned no jumper who could clear the gate or the fence.

Harry considered waking Johanna and telling her what had happened but decided against it. These mornings Johanna was sleeping a little later than usual because they were expecting another baby soon. He went outside and slipped into his wooden shoes. When he reached the paddock Snowman was frisking about. He circled the enclosure, swung around, and galloped in on a training barrier—a set of poles three feet high. He approached at an angle like a college athlete and hopped over the low jump, then galloped on. Harry laughed. No one would ever train a jumper to come in at such an angle. Snowman was certainly a self-made jumper.

Harry stirred himself. He had work to do before leaving for The Knox School stables. His thoughts were on the gray gelding as he cleaned the stables. He always thought best while doing such work. He liked the ammonia tang of a stall drain, the horsy odor of a stable. After he had tossed out the last forkful of litter and had tossed hay into the mangers and grain into the feedboxes, he went out into the paddock and whistled to Snowman. The gray gelding trotted to him. Harry patted a powerful shoulder.

"You want to be a jumper," he said softly. "I'll make a jumper out of you."

Of course, Harry admitted to himself, making a jumper out of this clumsy plow horse might not be an easy job, and, at best,

Snowman would hardly turn into better than a third-rate jumper. He had no class, no breeding; he wasn't sleek and high-tempered. He was built to pull a plow, keep his big feet on the ground and move ahead deliberately. But he looked as strong as any horse Harry had ever seen, and strength would carry a jumper a long way. In a grueling contest which might last a week, a horse needed power and strength.

He decided he would awaken Johanna. She would be eager to know what had happened. There had been much speculation after the first call from the doctor. He entered their bedroom and sat down on the edge of the bed. Johanna woke up and smiled at him.

"Anything wrong?" she asked sleepily.

"Snowman is back. He jumped the doctor's fence and ours, too." Harry grinned broadly.

"He jumped our fence?" Johanna looked startled.

"He trampled a lot of potato plants in a few fields. The doctor never wants to see him again." Harry's blue eyes twinkled.

"So you bought him back." A big smile formed on Johanna's lips.

"Yes," Harry said. "And I'm going to make a jumper out of him."

Johanna nodded her head. "There has always been something special about him."

"He isn't a jumper yet. He hits the barrier from the side. He may fall all over himself on some jumps." Harry was being cautious.

"You jumped with him already?" she asked.

"No, but I watched him jumping our training barriers just for fun."

They both laughed. The idea of a big plow horse jumping barriers for fun was absurd.

"You know you don't believe he'll fall all over himself," Johanna said.

"I guess not," Harry admitted.

"You're thinking of a champion," she said teasingly.

A faraway look came into Harry's eyes. "It could be," he said softly. "When I first saw him I had an odd feeling about him."

"Time the children were up. You better go tell them that Snowman is back to stay." Johanna pushed the covers back. She didn't want to miss the excitement she knew was coming.

Chef and Harriet and even Marty greeted the news with whoops. There was a wild scramble to get dressed and then a rush for the paddock. The children were swarming all over Snowman when Harry and Johanna arrived at the paddock.

Harry could not stay to join the party. He had stables to clean and horses to groom at the school so as to be ready for the day's classes.

It wasn't long before Harry had all of the evidence that he needed to convince him that Snowman did jump fences when he got bored with a pasture. The furor over the trampled potato plants brought reports from a number of people who had seen a big gray gelding leaping over walls and fences.

Visitors came to Hollandia Farm for a look at the gray horse who jumped fences by himself. None of them were impressed by what they saw, and some went away convinced that the whole thing was a publicity stunt pulled by Harry de Leyer to call attention to Hollandia Farm.

5 | Jumper

JUMPING is a branch of horsemanship in which cruel and un-
ethical methods of training are sometimes used—drugs, electric
spurs, and other devices designed to make a horse work against
his natural inclinations. Harry de Leyer wants no jumper that
has to be handled in such a way. If he can't win by firm kindness,
by gaining the trust of the horse, he feels he has failed. Being a
very determined and stubborn young man, he seldom fails. His
blue eyes turn chilly when he sees a horse abused. But he can be
rough with a horse that needs discipline or one that has been
spoiled by having his own way.

There was no need, in the case of Snowman, to win the trust
and confidence of the horse. They hit it off at once, probably
having laid a firm foundation that stormy February day outside

the New Holland auction ring. But patience was needed because Snowman had a lot to learn and some to unlearn. His self-taught approach had to be corrected. It would have resulted in disaster over high, wide jumps because it added to the distance which had to be cleared and exposed the hind legs to the top rail. Also, from the beginning, he was disdainful of low jumps. He was apt to knock down the top pole of a three-foot jump. High fences and gates seemed to challenge and arouse him. He took them with ease. He did not learn fast, but Harry did not hurry him. He believed a jumper should come along slow and not burn himself out under pressure.

In open jumping the performance of a horse is all that counts. The rules call for a loss of points called a "fault" if a horse touches a pole or knocks one down with fore- or hind feet, refuses to take a barrier, or unsaddles his rider, or leaves the course. Scoring is made on a point basis: five for first, three for second, two for third, and one for fourth place. These rules govern most American jumper contests, though at some shows the International rules are used.

The faults are classed as: a hind touch, meaning the hind foot touches the barrier—which calls for a half fault; a front touch, meaning the forefeet touch the barrier—this calls for one fault; knocking down a pole with the hind feet—which calls for two faults; and knocking down a pole with the forefeet—which calls for four faults. A first refusal, for taking a barrier or bolting from the course, calls for three faults. A second refusal calls for six faults. A third refusal eliminates the horse. Landing in water or a ditch or knocking down an object before or beyond the water calls for two faults if done with the hind feet and four faults if done with the forefeet. The fall of a rider or horse calls for elimination. The jumper with the lowest number of faults is the winner.

Snowman had to learn that sloppy work on any obstacle could

not be tolerated. Touches and knockdowns would cost him faults which would not only cut down his points but might lose him the event. Harry slowly and carefully introduced him to the obstacles he would face at a show: the coop, which looks like an A-roofed chicken house; the rail, which is a rail suspended between two posts; the gate, which is just that, a gate with bars; natural rails, which are two posts with rails between them; brush and fence, which is a rail fence with brush piled on each side. An aiken is a fenced-in hedge with the brush above the top of the rails. The hog's back is a set of three rails with the center rail higher than the others. The brush and rails is an aiken with the rails on each side set at some distance from the obstacle. Rails are a set of rails set parallel and some distance apart. Many of the obstacles are wide, some as much as six feet. The jumps all resemble obstacles a horse might meet in a cross-country run.

Snowman could easily qualify as an open jumper, because in this class breeding and height do not count. The sole determining factor is the horse's ability to jump over an object without touching it or knocking down any part of it. There are tough contests such as knock-down-and-out and touch and out. In these a touch or knockdown eliminates the horse.

To become a real competitor, Snowman had to learn to jump high and wide and clean. The obstacles on a course are designed to present a formidable, yet inviting appearance to a horse. In many cases, they are massive and oddly shaped, and many are painted in vivid colors and designs. In small arenas such as Madison Square Garden, they cross back and forth, providing many turns, with some of the barriers very close together. The jumps are planned to give thrills to the spectator, so none of them are easy. In case of a tie the rails are raised for the jump-off and may go as high as six feet or over.

Probably no one but Harry de Leyer would have had the persistence and patience to spend hours and days and weeks teaching an easy-going plow horse to face such a formidable task as mastering all of the obstacles in a championship show. Harry took the time, and he brought Snowman along slowly, building up his power and endurance, teaching him that every jump had to be his best. Form was not the biggest problem. Like a natural baseball batter, Snowman had form. When he ran he paced naturally, arching his neck and moving his head in rhythm with the beat of his hoofs. He might appear to be taking it easy as he headed toward a barrier, but he knew instinctively when he

needed to apply the speed and power which would carry him high and far.

Chef and Harriet exercised Snowman. Marty, who was growing fast, rode him. The big gray gelding liked them all and thoroughly enjoyed the attention they gave him. Harry did not call attention to his gray jumper. He knew that horse fanciers would laugh at Snowman and make jokes about him. Visitors who saw him seldom gave him a second look.

Harry no longer used Snowman as a riding horse. He wanted him around so that, when he had a little free time, he could use it to sharpen the gray's jumping, to teach him to respond instantly to a guiding knee or rein or to a word.

Harry knew that Snowman had been eight years old when he first bought him. He had checked the gelding's teeth carefully. In a horse, eight years places him in the same class as a boxer who has passed his fortieth year and is ready to retire. But that did not worry Harry. The big gray was full of life and was gaining power every day.

As Snowman came along, Harry rented him to men who wanted a sure-footed and easily handled hunter for a day's outing or a chase. He was the perfect horse for hunting, when dependability counts and when a rider does not want a horse he has to fight to keep taking hedges and water hazards. It would have seemed that Snowman would have better served as a hunter. There was one thing against that. Snowman couldn't compete in a show as a hunter, but he could as a jumper.

Harry also let some of his girls enter the big horse in junior shows so that he could get the feel of competing. Snowman never did anything spectacular in these shows. He won a few ribbons, collected a few faults because the low barriers offered no challenge. But life was becoming a big adventure for the gray gelding. He worked hard when he trained but now he had good food and grooming. He was sleek and smooth-haired. Best of all, he was developing spirit, showing a certain calm zest for life.

The relationship between Harry de Leyer and Snowman developed into tenderness and understanding. Any careful observer would have seen it in the way Snowman looked at Harry, and in the way Harry talked to the horse. It was apparent, too, in the way Snowman responded to anything Harry wanted him to do. The big gray had done little to raise Harry's hopes that he might have a champion, but he had captured Harry's affection.

With the arrival of William, the De Leyer brood increased to four blond, blue-eyed children who could have passed for natives back in Harry's home town. The rest of the clan were sure that William would grow up to be a horse lover. Wasn't he a De Leyer?

Chef, Harriet, and Johanna—even Marty—began to look forward to the day when Harry would announce that he was entering Snowman in a big show. Spring was fading away, and the leading jumpers were piling up points toward the Professional Horsemen's Association championship. But Harry kept his own council, and set to work with the gelding. Snowman faced the coop, brush and rails, the hog's back—all of the barriers a jumper faces in a top show. The gate gradually became higher, the obstacles wider. Snowman continued to go up and over. He knocked off a few rails and had a few touches, but he never refused a barrier or bolted, and he never fell.

One thing Harry did on some of the high jumps was to give Snowman a free rein. This would have lifted the eyebrows of trainers and horse owners who specialized in jumpers. They might have said that he did it so that later he could put on a showy act. But that was not his reason. He wanted to develop self-confidence in the gray gelding, to make the horse feel that he alone was responsible for the jump. Harry would be there with touch and voice, but it was Snowman who made the jump.

And so the days passed, with Snowman eagerly leaping over

barriers and occasionally jumping in a junior show. He hadn't changed much except for his form when he closed on a barrier. Then he was a confident and powerful machine, working smoothly, with timing which put him up and over the highest of the jumps. His faults became fewer with each training run.

6 | Sands Point

NO rider as good as Harry de Leyer goes unnoticed among professional horse fanciers. He had friends among the trainers and the stable managers, but he wasn't a part of the horse elite, the wealthy people who owned horses and entered them in the big-time shows on the circuit. He was a friend of Dave Kelly, trainer of Ben Duffy's horses. Kelly had ridden in many shows against Harry de Leyer, and a real friendship existed between them. Harry did not have the reputation Dave enjoyed. Dave rode the great mare, Andante, twice national horse-of-the-year and a real champion. Andante was expected to win the championship at Sands Point, one of the really big horse shows of the eastern circuit. It was Sands Point that Harry picked as a test for Snowman. His family excitedly welcomed his selection. Snowman could hold his own there; they were sure of it.

The Sands Point show is noted for its rugged jumping course. Only a really good horse has a chance there. Twenty veteran jumpers were entered in 1958. In addition to Andante there were Saxon Wood, Bellaire, and Red Lantern—to name a few of the best. All had been champions at many shows.

The Sands Point show is held on Long Island near New York City. A neighbor woman would care for baby William. This was to be a big occasion for the De Leyer clan. They were all out and busy long before daylight the morning the show opened. They clopped around the stable in their wooden shoes, helping Harry and his two grooms get the stable cleaned, the stay-at-home horses cared for and the tack ready for loading. They made a small ceremony out of loading Snowman; then all hurried to the house to change into party clothes, except Harry and the two grooms, who had more work to do. Harry would change at the show stalls.

Snowman took the whole affair more calmly than the family. He was eager to go because he had learned that at the end of a trailer ride there would be jumping, but he wasn't nervous or excited. He watched the loading of the other horses with interest and he watched the return of the dressed-up family to the station wagon.

"I wish I could be as calm as he is," Johanna said as she hurried across the yard after giving final instructions to the neighbor woman.

"I hope Andante gets lost," Chef said.

"Or Dave gets sick," Harriet added.

"No danger of either happening," Harry said. He started the engine and turned on the headlights. One of the grooms switched off the yard lights, and they were off.

Harry had been up since before four o'clock that morning. He had more than just Snowman to get ready. He was moving a small caravan to Sands Point. He had entered his young chest-nut mare, Wayward Wind, in the stake for first-year green

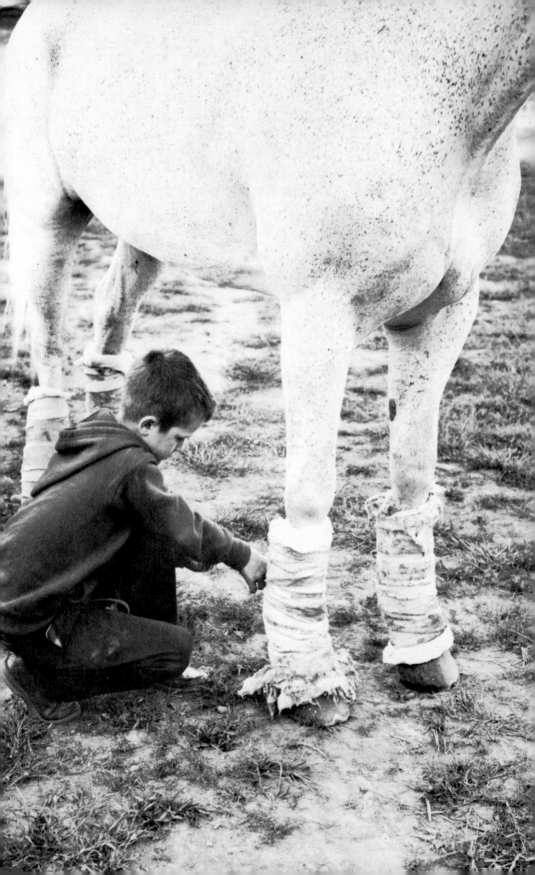

hunters and his gelding, Cicero, in the stake class for second-year green hunters. He had also agreed to ride an unruly mare which he stabled for Luisa Villegas, a girl from The Knox School. Harry felt responsible for the mare Night Arrest. He had taken over the job of curing her of some of her bad habits, and had learned that she couldn't be trusted. He was afraid to ask anyone to ride her, so he rode her himself. That made four horses from the Hollandia Stable. But if he was going to the big show, he might as well have four entries. For three days he would be a very busy man.

There were a thousand horses entered in the Sands Point show, but it would move along smoothly through the three days.

With so many horses and riders entered, only the famous and best-known horses and riders would interest the spectators who lined the fence or sat in the bleachers or in their sports cars. A rural, country-fair flavor always exists at this show. The crowd would be no mixed, tense assembly such as would be found at a race track. Any betting that was carried on was unorganized, a matter between friends. There were as many children and teen-agers as there were adults in the crowd. White-gloved hands leafed through tasseled programs. Johanna sat in the bleachers, but Chef, Harriet, and Marty perched on the top rail of the fence close to the gate through which the horses entered the field. Behind the fence were rows of stalls housing the entries.

Those in attendance at the show came because they loved good horses as much as because they expected to see thrills and spills. No one was keyed up; there wasn't going to be any daily double; no horse would win a fabulous purse. Snowman would be on twice each day as an open jumper. The crowd liked best the hunters and the jumpers. There was more action in these events, especially in the open-jumper event. Chef and Harriet and Marty would be pulling strong for Snowman, but they would also be cheering for Wayward Wind, Cicero, and Night Arrest.

Harry's first ride was on Wayward Wind in the first-year green hunter contest. The mare had not been in a show before the past January, so was eligible for that class. The highest jump was three feet six inches, and the hunters would be scored fifty per cent on conformation, form, and action, and fifty per cent on performance. Wayward Wind was a beautiful horse, and in 1958 she was showing signs of jumper ability which would take her out of the hunter class. Harry had trained her with care. She tossed her head as she swung around and headed for the first barrier. She took the jumps like a veteran. When the judges checked their score sheet she was the winner. A smiling Harry de Leyer acknowledged the polite applause which came from the crowd.

In the second-year green-hunter stake Harry rode Cicero, who had been in contests before. Cicero came through beautifully, winning the blue ribbon. Then Harry went on to win the green-jumper stake and the green-jumper championship on Luisa Villegas's Night Arrest. People began to thumb through their programs and to ask neighbors who the young man named Harry de Leyer was. He didn't seem to ride a horse so much as just to sit high atop of his mount. Word spread around that he was riding master at The Knox School near St. James and owner of a small stable, Hollandia Farm. All agreed that Harry de Leyer knew good horses and rode exceedingly well.

Chef and Harriet were tense as the open jumpers were paraded so that the crowd could see them. The open-jumper class was always the top event of the show, and there was keen interest in the thoroughbreds entered. Everyone was appraising the fine points of the spirited jumpers as they danced and high-stepped through the gate, shying and tossing their heads. Riders held their mounts tightly reined as the horses displayed their class and breeding by their eagerness and by fighting their bits and straining to be off. To a horse, the entries were all thoroughbreds, backs blanketed, fetlocks bandaged, aristocratic heads held high. Occasionally a horse would neigh defiantly and be brought up sharply by his rider. There was a sprinkling of trim young women among the riders. The onlookers murmured their approval, and there was a buzz of talk.

The buzz of talking died away, and the crowd sat staring at a broad-beamed farm horse as he ambled through the gate. They saw a big gelding of a shade of light gray, known among horsemen as "flea-bitten gray," walking placidly toward the thoroughbreds on a loose rein. Harry de Leyer guided the big gray to a position among the restless jumpers. Dozens of children, perched on the top rail, and many adults, forgot their manners enough to laugh out loud at the big-boned work horse making himself at home among the thoroughbreds. By now they knew the rider and were aware that this could hardly be a joke. Harry de Leyer was going to ride the comical-looking horse in the jumper event. The big gray seemed to enjoy the attention he was getting. His small ears were alertly pointed forward, and, since he was lightly held, he could and did turn his head to face the crowd lining the fence as if to examine them in a friendly way. A little girl, perched next to Chef, exclaimed, "Why, that funny old horse winked at me!"

Chef glanced at her disdainfully. "Sure, he did," he said loftily.

The field of laughter increased as the mass of spectators, rising from bleacher seats or standing up in Jaguars and Thunderbirds, sought to get a better look at the horses, especially the gray plow horse. White-gloved hands turned the pages of programs, looking for the name of the gray gelding. In a field of twenty willowy thoroughbreds he certainly stood out as an oddity. They found his name: Snowman, gray, standing two inches over sixteen hands. They shook their heads and smiled broadly. This was close to an insult to such horses as Andante, Sonora, and the seventeen others—all claiming illustrious bloodlines, all boasting body form which went with great jumpers.

The contenders jumping against Snowman were proven winners, tough contenders—the great Andante, twice winner and out to retire the trophy; Red Apple, reserve Champion for 1957. They held the attention of the crowd, which, after having its laugh, forgot the gray plow horse. One by one, the jumpers danced out through the gate to wait their turn at the course. Snowman trotted unhurriedly after them, swinging his head but holding it high.

Andante took an early lead, as was expected. The graceful jumpers showed their class as they took the course. There were faults and thrills as horses made spectacular jumps, or refused a barrier or fell, spilling a rider. Snowman jumped effortlessly and without any fuss and went unnoticed until the end of the second day. He picked up points but he wasn't exciting enough to draw attention. He swung along between barriers, hit the highest and the widest at just the right speed, went up and over them all. Most who watched the gray gelding closely did so because they expected him to plow into a tough barrier and go down amid flying poles, or scatter brush-and-rails. But he cleared them all with only a few faults, and those came on low and easy barriers. He had still to learn respect for even a three-foot six-inch hog's back or coop or rail. Harry talked to him and firmly controlled him, especially on the easy barriers.

So it went, with Andante flashing over the course, making a firm bid for the trophy, nursing her narrow lead carefully. Dave Kelly handled her like the expert that he is. Snowman came out for his last event of the day. Harry swung him around and headed him into the first barrier. He cleared it cleanly and flashed at his swinging gallop. He cleared every barrier easily until he came to the last one—a rail and brush. He galloped toward it and speeded up as he closed upon it, gaining the speed and power needed to clear it. As his forefeet lifted, Harry de Leyer leaned forward along his neck, the reins slack. The powerful hind legs gave their final thrust, and the gray body rose. The forelegs tucked in close together; the gray rump rose and arched cleanly over the ragged brush. But the hind feet came down with one of them inches too close. An iron shoe ripped down along a foreleg. It was a miscalculation of inches, but it inflicted an angry gash in Snowman's leg. Without breaking his stride, the gray gelding galloped on and swung toward the gate leading to the stalls.

There was polite applause, but no one except Harry and Johanna noticed the wound, which had just started to bleed. Harry leaned over, and what he saw as Snowman's forefeet flashed up and down made his lips tighten. Johanna hurried out of the bleachers.

On the top rail of the fence, Chef noticed as Snowman swung past. He gripped Harriet's hand.

"Snowman's foreleg is bleeding," he said, and leaped from the fence.

Harriet saw the blood and screamed, then jumped down and raced after Chef. Marty hopped down, and he, too, raced toward the stalls.

The crowd stirred and began to talk. The gray farm horse had at last roused their interest. He was now tied with the great Andante for first place. They knew as they watched him vanish that in the next day's final event the duel would be between this clumsy farm horse and the queen of the show. But, for Harry, that last jump, which had secured the tie, seemed to spell catastrophe. The leg could be expected to swell and stiffen during the night. There might even be permanent injury that would end the big gray's jumping career almost before it had got started. For now Harry knew that, barring injury, he had the makings of a champion in the big gray horse.

The family reached Snowman's stall just as Harry dismounted. They closed in around him and stared in horror at the raw and bleeding wound. Harry knelt and with gentle fingers probed for bone splinters of a fracture, any indication of permanent harm. There was none, but the leg would be badly swollen by morning.

"He's out of tomorrow's show," Johanna said sadly. "Just when he was about to be champion."

Harry shook his head grimly. He got to his feet and started uncinching the saddle. "We're not licked yet."

"You can put on a bandage," Harriet said hopefully.

"It's late for that," Harry said.

"You better get a vet," Chef said.

Marty moved close to Snowman and wrapped his arms around Snowman's sound leg. Tears squeezed out of his eyes as he looked up at the gray head above him. "It hurts," he said in a whisper. "It hurts."

Snowman lowered his head as though to assure the little boy that there was nothing to worry about. He turned the head toward Harry and seemed to include him in the assurance.

Johanna turned away slowly. She looked at the bare wall next to Snowman's stall. There probably wouldn't be any ribbons to tack on that wall.

Harry stacked the saddle and blanket. Johanna forced a smile. Harry shook his head grimly. "It's going to be a long night for me," he said.

Chef followed his father to the stall door. "What are you going to do now?" he asked.

"Clean up the wound and fix an ice pack," Harry answered. "I'll keep it filled all night."

Johanna, Harriet, and Marty left for their quarters. Chef stayed to help Harry. The two grooms cared for the other horses. There was no talk. They were almost as concerned as Harry was over the injury. They had counted on having a champion in Hollandia Stables.

Harry washed and disinfected the wound, then rubbed Snowman down and put a blanket on him. After making him comfortable in his stall, he and Chef started off to look for ice and materials for making a pack. They took the station wagon because Harry wanted a lot of ice.

At a filling station Harry bought a discarded inner tube; then they located a self-service ice dispenser where they bought several large sacks of ice cubes. The dispenser would be available at night so that he could get more ice if he needed it.

They returned to the stall, and Harry cut a length of inner tube and slipped it over Snowman's leg. He tied it at the bottom and then filled the tube with ice, leaving enough slack at the top so that the tube could be lashed securely and stay up on the leg.

Dinner that night was a gloomy affair. Johanna called home to see how William was getting along before she sat down.

"William all right?" Harry asked.

"Full of milk and asleep," Johanna said and smiled at Harry.

No one had much of an appetite except Marty. He had two helpings of potatoes and meat. Johanna was sure Snowman was out of competition, but she didn't talk about it. Harry looked so grim and determined that she knew he hadn't given up hope, and when he went at anything with such determination he usually succeeded. There had been many times when he had refused to be licked. Like the time he had dragged the fire hose along the wall with bullets zipping past his head. She almost laughed as she remembered the time he had handed her a flashlight when the ancient car's headlights refused to work. He had said to her, "Get in; we're going places." And they had gone.

When Harry pushed his chair back from the table Chef spoke up, "Can I go with you?"

"You have to get to bed early," Harry said.

"I could stay up until ten," Chef argued.

Harry smiled. He and Chef had always done a lot of things together. "Until ten," he said.

They returned to Snowman's stall and found the gray gelding standing patiently. His big head swung over the half door in greeting. His ears were cocked forward, and there was the usual bright gleam in his eyes. Harry patted his neck. "You big Teddy bear; you're going to beat Andante tomorrow."

"You sure are," Chef said.

Harry replenished the ice in the pack. He and Chef sat on camp stools close to the stall door. There was no talk, and both father and son dozed a little. At five minutes to ten o'clock Harry nodded to Chef.

"Time to be off to bed."

Chef got to his feet, leaned over the stall door, and spoke to Snowman, who was still standing. "Goodnight, you big lug," he said and turned quickly away.

Harry looked at the ice pack and refilled it with cubes. He stood at the door after he had finished. "No faults tomorrow," he said softly. "You'll beat Andante by watching your big feet on those low jumps."

Snowman extended his muzzle and pushed up against the door. Harry dug his fingers into the coarse hair of the gray's neck. Snowman responded with his usual grimace. Harry returned to his stool. He dozed a little, listening to the night sounds: the crickets and a distant frog-pond chorus, the sleepy protests from a bird something had disturbed. He roused himself at intervals and replenished the ice in the pack. A little after midnight he went to the ice dispenser for more cubes.

Sitting up all night would do his nerves and reflexes little good, but he had to do everything he could to keep Snowman's leg from swelling and stiffening. The night wore on, and each time Harry replenished the ice in the pack he talked to Snowman about how he would beat Andante the next day.

"We'll take them high and safe," or "If it comes to jump-offs, you can't fail; you're too big and strong for that mare."

Harry finally moved from the stool to the ground, where he sat with his back against the stable wall. Snowman lowered his head over the door so that his muzzle was close to Harry's shoulder. Man and horse relaxed, and Harry dropped off to sleep. He hadn't planned to sleep, and when he awakened he jerked forward and staggered to his feet. It was broad daylight, and he knew it was hours later than he usually awakened when at a show. He looked at his watch. The time was six o'clock. Snowman was watching him eagerly. It was long past the time when he usually got his oats. Other grooms were at work along the line. Night Arrest and Wayward Wind were not in their stalls. The grooms had taken them to water.

Harry opened the stall door and stepped inside. The tube on the wounded leg was limp and deflated, showing clearly that the ice from the last pack had melted. Snowman seemed to be resting his weight on both forelegs, not favoring the injured leg, but Harry was sure the horse had remained standing all night. He knelt down. For a moment or so he hesitated about loosening the thongs which held the tube in place. His fingers fumbled a little as he untied the knots. Slowly, carefully, he slid the tube off the injured leg.

Sensing a presence behind him, Harry turned his head. Johanna was standing at the open door, muffled in a housecoat, her hair in disarray, her blue eyes showing the concern she felt. She leaned forward and looked at the injured leg. Harry smiled up at her.

"No swelling," she said softly.

"Not a trace," Harry agreed.

But they both knew that the real test was yet to come. Harry stood up and took hold of Snowman's mane, pulling gently. Snowman moved out of the stall eagerly. Harry guided the gray across the street to a training paddock. Snowman entered the paddock eagerly. So far he had shown no sign of a limp. When Harry freed him he galloped away. Harry ran toward a barrier in the center of the paddock. Snowman saw where Harry was headed and swung about. He came in on the barrier at a lope and sailed over it.

Several passing grooms paused to look, surprised at seeing a free-running riderless horse taking a jump. Johanna hurried to

Harry's side. She threw her arms around him. "You have worked a miracle," she cried, her words broad with the Dutch accent because she was so excited.

Harry laughed. "The ice worked a miracle," he said, his eyes twinkling.

He wasn't sure whether it had been the ice or because he had kept telling the big gray that he'd beat Andante and how he'd go about doing it. He decided that he had better let the ice pack have the credit, so he didn't tell Johanna about talking to Snowman.

There was a possibility that when Snowman got on the grueling course the leg would give out on him, but that was a chance they had to take. Up to the time the open jumper event started Snowman would be kept moving. The big gray nickered. He wanted his oats.

"Sorry," Harry said. "You'll get your grain."

He and Johanna started off, with the gray gelding following close behind Harry. Soon he was munching oats happily.

Chef arrived, ready to help his mother exercise Snowman. He was as excited as his mother had been when he learned that the leg was not stiff or swollen. He shouted the news to Harriet when she appeared, followed by Marty.

"Snowman's good as new!"

Harriet rushed forward to see for herself. When she was convinced she danced up and down. "That fixes Andante," she announced.

Harry smiled. "We still have to beat her," he said seriously.

The time for the open-jumper event came. and Snowman had shown no signs of favoring his injured leg. Either Chef or Johanna had given him enough exercise to keep the leg limber. Everyone expected it to be a duel between Andante and Snowman. There was little chance that any other horse could win, though one of the others might cut down the leader's points enough to decide which would be champion. Most of the horse-men favored Andante. They still couldn't believe that an old plow horse could beat a thoroughbred when the final test came. Red-eyed and weary, Harry de Leyer sat and waited for Snow-man to be called to the course. He certainly wasn't feeling his best.

Andante came on before Snowman. She was in her usual faultless form. She pranced through the gate, and Dave Kelly let her have her little show before he swung her around and headed her into the first jump, a brush-rail barrier. She sped toward it, rose, and sailed over, then raced down the course to-ward the hog's back. Up she went and over, then swung wide and headed for a wall. She took the wall in an easy leap which wasted no energy, her hoofs missing the top pole only by inches. On she went, with Dave Kelly timing her perfectly at the wide jumps and the high barriers. There was a wave of applause as she cantered out through the gate.

When Snowman trotted through the gate there was no ap-

plause except from the children, who had begun to like the big gray gelding who always gave them a greeting as he passed the fence. They were aware that the looks he gave them were given because he liked children. Win or lose the youngsters were with him, and they let him know it by loud cheers.

Harry swung the big gray around and sent him toward the first jump. He moved in eagerly, swinging along with even strides. As Harry leaned forward along the gray neck, he knew that this first jump might tell the story. Up Snowman went, tucking his forefeet in, thrusting powerfully with his back legs. He took the barrier easily, handling his iron-shod hind feet with care. He went on to the four-foot-six brush rail and over it, then the four-foot-nine hog's back with its five-foot spread. Swinging around, he headed back into the wall. Harry had turned his head just a little as he landed so that he would not have to put a strain on the injured leg when he made his turn. He went up and over the white wall and shifted course to take the triple bars. Harry could not detect a single movement which would have indicated that Snowman was beginning to favor his right foreleg. He leaped high and clean over the triple bars and went on, sailing over the barriers in high, clean jumps. The crowd did not hold their breath when he went over as they had done when Andante took a jump. Snowman left plenty of daylight between his hoofs and a barrier. Facing the last barrier—a brush-and-rails with a height of five feet—Snowman had a chance to outpoint Andante if he made a clean jump.

Across the course he pounded toward the high barrier. He stretched his head out eagerly, tail rising a little, but not twisting or lashing as some nervous jumpers do with their tails. He gathered speed for the last jump. As was always the case with him, the higher the barrier the better he liked it and the more effort he made. His forefeet lifted as he closed on the barrier and tucked in neatly as his head and shoulders lifted. His powerful

back legs thrust. In a split second he was over in a clean, graceful arc of gray horseflesh.

For a space of time there was silence in the stands. Then the
youngsters started shouting and were joined by the crowd. The
clapping was not the polite patting together of white-gloved
hands; it was a rousing ovation. There was eager shouting and
whistling from the youngsters on the fence and in the hot rods
and sports cars. The elite of the horse world had taken a big
gray plow horse to their hearts. Here was the warmth and
romance of a fairy tale. A plain and ungraceful Cinderella had
become the belle of the ball. The world of horses and horse
people had watched an unheard-of upset.

Chef and Harriet leaped from the fence and raced away toward the stables, with little Marty doing his best and wasting
his breath shouting after them, "Wait . . . for me!"

Johanna was out of the stand, and she, too, was running. She
passed Andante's stall with its outside wall plastered with ribbons. The many colored strips of silk danced and fluttered in the
small wind which funneled between the stables. It also rustled
the green imitation grass on the little artificial lawn spread before
Andante's stall. Johanna felt a quick pang of sympathy for the
loser. Andante could have retired the trophy but for a big gray
gelding. The pang vanished as she reached Snowman's stall.

Harry was unsaddling the big horse, patting his neck and
shoulders, talking to him.

"I told you that you could do it." He looked sheepish as
Johanna rushed up to Snowman.

"He was wonderful." She patted Snowman's muzzle. "Our
champion," she said.

Chef and Harriet arrived and swarmed over Snowman.

"You big hero!" Harriet shouted.

"He's the champ," Chef added. "Nobody can beat him."

Marty arrived, angry and out of breath. He sputtered accusingly at Chef and Harriet, then hugged one of Snowman's legs.

"We'll walk him and rub him down," Chef offered.

Harry turned the lead rope over to them. Harriet held the rope while Chef got a blanket. Harry was glad of a chance to stretch out and relax. It had been a big day for him.

7 | Decision

HARRY DE LEYER was faced with a big decision after the Sands Point show, and he wasn't helped in deciding by what David Dillard had taught him regarding the best way to make money out of a horse farm. He had a prosperous business, not big, but steadily growing. He had never been a gambler; he had always done the safe sure thing, always making some profit on any horse he sold, always seeing to it that a horse earned his keep. Now he had to decide what he was going to do with Snowman.

He knew that in the gray gelding he had a potential national champion. But giving the big gray his chance at the national honors meant hitting the horse-show circuit in earnest, vanning to a new show each weekend—Westport, Lakeville, Branchville, Smithtown, Stony Brook, Piping Rock, Paramus, Harrisburg,

Washington. The horse-show circuit is a wealthy man's sport. There would be big entry fees, travel expenses, days of riding his heart out. It would be a long, tiring summer, with an autumn which could very well end in heavy losses. At best there were only small purses. If a jumper missed the one big purse, he could earn very little. The usual open-jumper purse is seldom as much as fifty dollars. And for the first time in his life Harry was faced with a health problem. A spot on his tongue had begun to pain and bother him. It wasn't something that disabled him but it failed to heal up.

The decision concerned Johanna and the children. It called for a serious talk with his wife. The boys and Harriet would be all-out for giving Snowman his chance. They idolized the big fellow and already considered him a world champion. They would be eager to hit the circuit trail. It would be one big adventure after another, at least up until school started in the fall. But Johanna's thrifty Dutch nature might prompt her to object. If she did, there weren't any logical arguments in his favor. He'd have to admit the idea was a gamble on long odds. He picked a time when the boys and Harriet were out of the house to talk with her about it.

Johanna knew what was coming; she had known since Sands Point. She had known the moment Snowman cleared the last barrier in the final jumper event and beat Andante, but she had waited until Harry was ready to talk about it. She was working at her mending when Harry entered the living room with a cold bottle of cola in his hand. Hesitating, he offered the bottle to her.

"I'll get another for myself," he said quickly.

Johanna took the frosty bottle. She smiled at him. "I'd like a glass, too."

Harry grinned. "I forgot that you don't like to drink out of a bottle." He hurried off as though relieved and eager to get away.

He returned with his bottle and with a glass for Johanna. He sat down beside her on the davenport and waited until she had filled her glass before he took a deep drink. Then he said abruptly, "About Snowman." He hesitated.

"He could be a national champion." She looked thoughtfully at the bubbles drifting upward in her glass and smiled.

"I think so," Harry said eagerly. "He has the heart, the strength." He took another deep drink.

"Madison Square Garden," Johanna said dreamily.

Harry grinned broadly. He had been doing a lot of dreaming himself since Sands Point. He was happy, too, because he knew now that Johanna wasn't going to be a problem. He nodded his head quickly.

"It would mean a long hard summer and fall. I can't ask you and the children to rough it with me." He finished the cola and set the bottle on the floor.

"And you can't keep us from being with you as much as we can manage." She gave him an impish smile.

Solid and stubborn as he was, Harry could never resist that smile. It had won his heart back in St. Oedenrode when they were school kids. Also, he liked to have Johanna and the children with him. Harry was a family man who liked to work with his children. He planned to make a real horse expert out of Chef, and the shows would be a good education for the boy. A show had always been a family project, the same as running the riding stable.

"You wouldn't have to take them all in," he said.

Johanna gave him another smile. She'd decide for herself. She had little William to think about as well as Chef, Harriet, and Marty. They would want to attend every show, even if it meant cutting school.

"Snowman has to have his chance," she said, ducking the question of how much time she could spend at the shows.

"I feel that way, too," Harry said.

Johanna picked up her mending. Harry got to his feet. He had work to do. Now that the decision had been made he would have a lot of work to do. As he walked out of the house, he thought that he had always known Snowman would get his chance to be champion. He had become so attached to the big gray that the financial gamble seemed a small matter, a reasonable thing to do. He wouldn't have tried it with Cicero or Wayward Wind; he didn't have the same feeling for them, the personal closeness he felt for Snowman.

Once they had decided to hit the horse-show circuit, the family gave much of their attention to plans and preparations for traveling. Of course, business at Hollandia Farm had to go on; that would not be neglected. Harry had a groom and a young man who was learning to be a groom. He'd have to add some help because the pair would have to travel with him on weekends. Chef and Harriet could do many things. Johanna could make a deal with the neighbor woman for more of her time. Busy as he was, Harry found time to work with Snowman. He had always been a hard worker, but now he found himself busier than he had ever been in his life.

The first show would be at Westport, Connecticut, in the latter part of June. Everything went along smoothly, except the spot on Harry's tongue, which continued to bother him in spite of the home medicines he used. He kept telling himself that the spot would clear up. He had had sores and cuts before, and they had always healed in time.

The Fairfield County Hunt Club Show at Westport was scheduled for four days. It would be Snowman's second tough test, and one which might determine the fate of Harry's summer plans. A bad showing at Westport would make the success of the venture very doubtful. It would build up the gambling odds.

Harry's standing with the Fairfield Hunt Club was that of a young outsider who was presuming to break into a very elite circle of horseflesh with a horse the membership would con-

sider much less than desirable, a plow horse without conformation or blue blood. This didn't bother Harry; he wasn't out to
win the approval of a group of horse fanciers. His sole concern
was for Snowman. He was after points, a lot of them. His big
gray was starting after many of the top jumpers had already
piled up points. Dave Kelly would be the only close friend he'd
have at the show.

Harry should have had plenty to worry about, but he just
wasn't the worrying kind. The Oak Ridge stables were considered by all of the sports writers as sure winners in the open-
jumper competition. Their two jumpers—First Chance and
Sonora—had been in four shows that spring and had won
championships and reserve honors in all of the shows. At Oak
Ridge the previous week, Oak Ridge horses had taken honors in
seven out of eight contests. The writers went on predicting.
They ignored Harry de Leyer's gray gelding. Harry just went
on sharpening Snowman's form, getting travel detail and entry
paper work out of the way. Chef and Harriet blissfully discussed
the series of triumphs Snowman would have. They knew most of
the contenders, and Chef could recite their records.

The first day of the meet Harry wasn't rushed. He expected
the second day to start things going for Snowman. He was
riding Night Arrest in the green-jumper class for Luisa Villegas,
and that was always a test of horsemanship. Night Arrest was
a wild little mare with a nervous body and a head full of wild
ideas. She would not have been entered in any show if Harry
hadn't agreed to ride her. He didn't trust her, but he managed
to ride her to a second place in the first day's green-jumper
event, by checking and controlling her as she came into each
jump.

A heavy rain made the course a quagmire for the second day.
Harry had no way of knowing how Snowman would act in the
mud. He had big feet and had once been very clumsy at
handling them. He might very well slip and knock down a few

rails. Certainly the high, wide jumps would be treacherous, actually dangerous.

Snowman's strongest rival in the knock-down-and-out event was his former rival, Andante. With Dave Kelly riding her, she would be a threat. In the first round, twelve horses managed to go clean, but in the jump-off, with the rails raised, only Andante and Snowman had faultless rounds. Snowman had demonstrated that he was a mudder. He planted his feet carefully and set them before he left the ground. Harry was surprised and pleased. The rails were again raised. Waiting at the gate, Harry patted Snowman's neck and talked to the big gray.

"High and wide. You go way up this time," he said. "Use that old power, Teddy bear."

Snowman might go clean again but so might Andante. She was in her finest form. The third jump-off would be to her advantage because then time would count and she is a fast horse. The day had been a rough one on the gray gelding, and on the third day he faced a tougher test—the open-jumper contest. That one Harry wanted because it would make Snowman champion of the show.

Andante went first, and, as Harry had thought she might, she had a clean round. Harry trotted Snowman into the field and swung him around to face the first barrier. As the big gray picked up speed and closed on the barrier, Harry nudged him with a knee. Immediately obedient, Snowman swerved off course and headed for a hog's back. The crowd muttered, and many shouted warnings, thinking the gray gelding or Harry had become confused about the course flags. But it wasn't a mistake. Harry was simply letting Andante win by default so that there would not have to be a third jump-off which might tire Snowman so much that he wouldn't be in shape for the big jumper event the next day. A horn sounded; Snowman was out. He had sacrificed two points in settling for second place. He snorted and shook his head, as near to angry disobedience as he

ever came. He wanted to jump those high barriers. For him, this event had begun to be interesting. Harry patted his neck as he headed him toward the stables.

Johanna understood what Harry had done and why, but Chef and Harriet were brokenhearted. Their Snowman had been beaten by Andante without taking a single barrier. They didn't reproach the gray gelding, but Harriet talked to him, explaining the terrible results when a horse heads for the wrong barrier.

Chef became a little suspicious when his father laughingly said, "He won't do it again."

"He better not tomorrow," Chef muttered.

Marty got a strap to spank the horse, but Chef took it away from him. "You never hit a horse. Riders who use a whip make their jumpers knock down poles."

The course for the open-jumper event the next day was so bad it seemed unlikely that any horse would make a round without faults or spills due to skidding into a barrier. Harry and Snowman came out on call and waited at the gate. Snowman had proved that he was a good mudder, but today's course was bad, even for such a horse. Horses floundered and brought down rails; several refused to jump, and there had been two nasty spills. None had so far posted a clean round. Kimberton Vike had the best record, with two faults.

Harry trotted Snowman through the gate, as it opened, and circled, heading him into the first jump of the big event. The big gray shook his head and swung off across the muddy field. He splashed through a deep pond, sending muddy water flying. His long strides quickened as he closed upon the barrier, a four-foot-six-gate brush jump. His forelegs lifted and tucked in; his muzzle stretched out, and his hind legs corded as his hoofs sank into the soft ground, seeking solid footing. He went up and over clean, and he did not skid when he landed. Harry de Leyer had his head turned into the next jump before his forefeet hit the soggy ground. On he went, up and over the next barrier. He made it look as easy in the mud as it was on dry ground or turf. He sailed over the five-foot gate and over the painted wall. He cleared the last barrier—a rail brush with a wide spread—and swung away from the course with just one half of a fault against him. It was a convincing exhibition. The gray plow horse seemed to have everything.

The crowd was enthusiastic; they were now all for the gray gelding. He could still be beaten, but few in the crowd believed

that would happen, even though First Chance—Oak Ridge's
entry—was coming out for his round, and before the show First
Chance had been a favorite.

First Chance turned in a sparkling performance, but Snowman had a three-point lead. In his round the gray had shaken
off the last vestige of a lazy, easy-going approach and had
jumped as though he didn't want to waste any time in getting
over the course.

Snowman seemed to like the roar of approval which greeted
him as Harry led him out to accept the ribbon. He was show
champion and appeared to know it. He lifted his head and looked
at the people in the stands. They waved and shouted.

Harry de Leyer and Johanna were on the way, their faces turned toward Madison Square Garden. Nothing short of a broken leg could have kept them away from Lakeville. Snowman had started piling up points toward a national record. They had confidence that the big gray would go all of the way. Chef and Harriet were certain. They admitted none of the hazards Harry and Johanna knew lay ahead.

"They will put a swell blanket on him at the Garden when they bring him out," Chef said.

"He'll get a real trophy, not just a ribbon, I bet," Harriet added.

"Shucks, yes, maybe two."

"And a lot of money." Harriet danced over to Snowman's stall and patted the gray's cheek.

Harry was backing the trailer around. He poked his head out and shouted, "Clear the way!"

Harriet and Chef jumped aside. Marty, who had been lying on a hay bale, hopped off. He was eager to be on the way home. After they were loaded up, Harry would buy them all hamburgers which they could munch on the ride home.

Chef looked at the few ribbons Johanna was removing from the stable wall. "Before we get through we'll have enough ribbons to cover that wall," he said.

"Two walls." Harriet skipped toward the truck. She, too, was thinking about hamburgers.

Snowman began to make the headlines with the Westport show over. A headline in *The New York Times* for July twenty-first announced that Harry de Leyer's Snowman, an odd-looking gray gelding, had carried off the open-jumper honors at the Lakeville Horse Show. It also announced that Harry had won the reserve championship on Night Arrest. Luisa's wild little mare had come through again. And each sports writer had to retell the gray gelding's story about his beginning. They called him "De Leyer's Eighty-Dollar Horse" and "Fugitive from a Cannery" or "The Cinderella Horse." There was an argument between Marie Lafrenz of the *Herald Tribune* and George Coleman of the *Sun* which became almost a duel. Marie was all for Snowman; she loved the big gray gelding and believed in him. George admitted Snowman was quite a horse, but doubted his ability to come through the grueling tests the circuit offered, and, if he did get to Madison Square Garden, the gray could not win the championship. Most of the writers contented themselves by saying that Harry de Leyer kept on winning titles that he shouldn't. They said that the former Junior Olympic rider and his eighty-dollar horse were not working according to the book.

Then the De Leyer caravan arrived at Brookville, and Brookville wasn't all roses. Harry's tongue was really giving him trouble. He was finding it hard to eat anything but soft foods, soup, and other liquids. His tough body was getting jumpy, and he was also finding it difficult to keep his family from noticing that all was not well with him. He fooled Chef and Harriet, but he didn't fool Johanna. A wife knows when anything serious goes wrong with the man she loves.

But Harry was too busy to go see a doctor. His stubborn streak was working. Snowman was piling up points, winning championships. It was on to Smithtown and more victories. He wouldn't let the big horse down. Snowman was more now to Harry than just a gray plow horse; he was a symbol of all that Harry de Leyer had dreamed of; he had a destiny to fulfill, and Harry was part of it.

So it went on, with each week bringing its test of man and rider, along the rugged course which led to the big show.

8 | Big Trouble

DURING the week before the Branchville Horse Show Harry was able to eat very little. He was weak and shaky as the opening day drew near, but he was determined to carry on. Snowman was having a winning streak, and he would not break it. No one had ever ridden the gray gelding in championship competition. He and the big jumper were as one, coordinated, responsive to each other. It was a close, intimate relationship which, if it was upset, might throw Snowman off his form enough to start him losing. No one knew better than Harry de Leyer how close that margin could be. A fine jumper may suddenly lose his timing, his feel for height and distance, his ability to pace himself so as to be set for each barrier. He was sure that he had much to do with the gray jumper's wonderful timing.

When the show opened Harry and Snowman faced a wet and

muddy course which would be difficult. Harry's tongue was swollen, and he was in constant pain. The sky above the grounds was heavy with threatening clouds; the weather prediction was for more rain.

The first day Snowman did not do well. Harry was certain it was all his fault. He hadn't given the gray gelding the help he needed and expected. There was a night program, with rain threatening. As Harry and Snowman came out for the open-jumper event black thunder clouds were rolling in, the sky was torn open by lightning, thunder shook the stands, and sheets

of rain came down. Snowman faced a course mottled with pools and puddles. Rain pelted him, and, above, the air was in a tumult.

Snowman pivoted in the mud and headed for the first jump, a high brush-rail barrier. He sailed over the barrier and landed with a splash, dirty water showering up, around, and over him. He shook the water from his head as Harry guided him toward the four-foot-nine-inch rails. Harry gave the big fellow his head. It was up to Snowman. Harry was too weak to offer much help, but he was staying on Snowman's back and hoping for the best. The big gray did as he always did; he went into the barrier at what seemed a slow pace, as though he knew he had the power to make the jump without a furious burst of speed. But this time he did put on speed, possibly considering a foot-deep pool of water before the barrier. His forefeet tucked in as they rose. At that instant a ragged bolt of lightning, close overhead, slashed through the rain, and the lights went down, then out, and the course was swallowed by black night. Harry leaned far forward and set himself for a bad spill. Snowman's hind feet hit the water and found solid ground, hock deep in muddy water. Not being able to see the rail, he had to jump as high and as far as he could. Later, Harry said he was sure the old boy jumped seven feet high. Up the gray body went, hind feet extended, then drawn in for the landing. He landed running, and plunged into the black wall ahead of him.

A flash of lightning revealed the next barrier only a few yards away. Harry started to curb the big horse, to swing him off course. After all, Snowman didn't have infrared eyes, and they were closing on a nasty four-foot-nine wall. Suddenly the lights came back up, as they often do when dimmed by a bolt of lightning. The gray gelding went up and over the wall without breaking his stride. A roar went up from the crowd of damp spectators. They had expected to hear a crash as the gray hit the wall.

Snowman sailed on, leaping high and clean over the barriers, drenching himself and Harry with mucky water, shaking the rain from his face, stretching his head out, ears pricked forward. He was having a ball; no one who watched him could feel otherwise. He looked like something out of a mud bath, his gray coloring now a deep brown. He flashed over the last barrier and swung toward the gate. He had done well and would earn points on the round, and he had given the people in the bleachers a thrill when he made the blind jump and had not faltered or swung off course. The crowd was glad they had refused to let the storm drive them out of the stands.

Disaster struck later in the show. Harry was so weak he could hardly climb into the saddle when the time came to ride Snowman. The big gray knocked off rails and earned so many faults that he was out of the money. Harry was sure it was his failure and not Snowman's. It was a bad day for the gray gelding's championship hopes. Harry felt very low in spirits as he drove home. He knew he could not go on at the Smithtown show and began to think that this was the end of his dream to make the big horse a national champion, the end of the De Leyer clan's hope of getting to Madison Square Garden.

When he got home, he called his friend Dave Kelly and told him his troubles. He knew he could depend upon Dave's advice. Dave would be riding Andante at Smithtown. The mare was well up near the top in points. But Dave might be able to suggest a rider Harry could get. He himself could think of no one he thought capable of getting the best out of Snowman, which was what would be needed to win.

Johanna was now fully aware of how sick Harry was and wanted him to see a doctor. She was glad he had finally admitted he could not go on and had to have help.

"Just wanted you to know that you won't have to worry about Snowman," Harry said when he got Dave on the phone. His voice was thick because of his swollen tongue. Then he went on to tell Dave what the situation was.

There was a few minutes' silence at the other end of the line; then Dave said, "You're not taking that horse out of competition now. I'll ride him."

"But you have Andante in the jumper stake," Harry said quickly.

"No reason why I can't ride both." Dave laughed. "If you care to risk it."

"It would be no risk," Harry said. "You never pulled a horse in your life."

"Thanks," Dave said. "Then it's settled."

There was a little more talk, but Dave won out. Harry was shaking his head when he went to tell Johanna. She was excited because Dave was perhaps the best professional rider in that part of the country. But her main concern was about Harry.

"Now you can go see the doctor," she said.

"I guess I had better," Harry mumbled. "I'll do it right away." He tried to smile. "Dave Kelly is the only man I'd want to ride Snowman."

Harry went to see his doctor at once. He wasn't worried about himself, but he was annoyed and irritated because the tongue trouble was upsetting his plans. He wanted it over with and cleared up fast. He couldn't expect Dave Kelly to ride Snowman in the remaining shows. That would not be fair to Dave or to Andante.

Harry was in the doctor's examining room only a short time. Then the doctor took him to his office, and Harry sat down. The doctor made a few notes on a pad, then said abruptly, "You have a tumor. It will have to come out at once. I'll make arrangements at the hospital. You won't have to stay there but you'll need to rest for a few days."

"A tumor?" Harry stared at the doctor. "It could be serious?" he asked anxiously.

"Yes," the doctor admitted. "But we won't borrow trouble. I'll send some of the tissue to the laboratory. We'll wait and see."

The doctor took a sample of the tumor tissue. Harry went home to wait. Not wanting to upset Johanna, he simply told her that he had to go to the hospital and have the growth on his tongue removed at once. He wanted to get it over with so he could get back to handling Snowman. Johanna kept her worries to herself and helped him get ready for the operation. And she saw to it that he rested and did not work at the stable. Harry isn't an easy man to make relax, but Johanna managed to get him to rest.

The operation itself was not a serious one. Harry was on his way home within a few hours after entering the hospital. His mouth was sore, but he felt better with the tumor removed. When he left the hospital the doctor said, "I'll be in touch with you after I receive the laboratory report."

Johanna had gone to the hospital with Harry. She turned to the doctor and gave him an anxious look. She had suddenly realized that something serious might happen. Before she could ask any question, the doctor handed Harry a prescription and said, "Get this filled. Rest and try to eat as much solid food as you can. And don't start worrying about anything." He smiled at Harry. "Don't ride again until I have checked you over."

Harry and Johanna did not talk much on the way to the drug store. For one thing, Harry's mouth was bandaged, and so it was not easy to use his tongue. On the way home they talked a little, but not about the operation. Harry's mind was on Snowman. He would keep a close watch on the gelding's progress with Dave Kelly riding him. He was conscious of a feeling of jealousy because Dave was going to handle Snowman at Smithtown. As they turned in at the Hollandia Farm gate, he said, "I feel better already. I'll be riding that big boy in the Stony Brook show."

"And Snowman will be back winning," Johanna said firmly. She squeezed Harry's arm eagerly. Nothing must happen to upset the summer which had started so gloriously. It wouldn't be fair to Harry or to Snowman.

The operation had been on Tuesday. For three days Harry tried to rest, but it was hard to keep from working with the gray gelding. He poked around the stable, lazed in the sun, and he ate heartily. The grooms could do the many things which needed doing in order to have Snowman ready for Smithtown. Night Arrest was not entered, and Wayward Wind would not compete. But Snowman had to go the rounds in order to stay in the race for points. All Dave Kelly could be expected to do was to ride the gray in the show. Harry had confidence in Dave. He had watched Snowman jump at all of the shows where he had been entered. But Harry could not help feeling that Dave wouldn't be able to get as much out of the gray gelding as he could.

On Saturday Harry had an appointment with the doctor. His tongue would be checked and so would his fitness to return to the saddle. Johanna went with him, prompted by an uneasy feeling she could not explain. After a few minutes' wait the nurse took them directly to the doctor's office. Harry had expected to go to the examination room. The doctor greeted them with his best professional smile.

"Good morning, Johanna, Harry." He nodded toward chairs close to his desk. "Please be seated."

They sat down, and the doctor returned to the chair behind his desk. He pulled a sheet of paper toward him and studied it, a small frown forming on his lips. Then he said, looking at Harry, "Do you have anyone who can take charge of your affairs, Harry?"

Puzzled, Harry was silent for a minute. "No," he said. "Why do you ask?"

The doctor glanced down at the paper before him, hesitated a few moments, then said, "I have just received the report on the tissue from your tongue. It arrived from the laboratory less than an hour ago." He cleared his throat. He seemed to be making a decision. At last he said, "The tumor was malignant."

Both Harry and Johanna stared at the doctor, unable to grasp at once the significance of his words. Finally Harry spoke. "Cancer?"

The doctor nodded. "I'll have to operate again and at once. I would say it must be done in three days."

"How serious is it?" Johanna managed to ask. The dread word "cancer" had shocked her into a state of numbness, but both she and Harry came from strong stock, hardy stock, with courage one of their main assets.

"I'll have to take more than half of the tongue to make sure we remove all of the malignant cells," the doctor said cautiously.

"What will that mean to me?" Harry asked.

"You will never again have normal speech. In time you will learn to communicate in a limited way." The doctor showed his concern. "In the case of a malignant tumor there is no way of being sure that all the cells have been removed. You will have to let me keep you under close care for a long time, I'm afraid."

"I can't go on with the horse farm?" Harry asked.

"I'm afraid not. We must not take any unnecessary chances," the doctor said gravely.

Harry got to his feet slowly. Johanna rose and stood close to him. Harry said dully, "I'll report to the hospital in three days."

"Everything will be ready." The doctor stood behind his desk watching them with concern. "I'll have a specialist to work with me."

Without another word, Johanna and Harry left the doctor's office. Johanna's hand was firmly on Harry's arm as they walked out of the building and across the sidewalk to the station wagon. Harry got in, and Johanna followed, moving close to him. He pressed the starter button and sat listening to the engine for a few seconds before he shifted into low gear and drove away.

At first they felt only dull shock; then the realization struck them like a massive blow that this was the end of the life Harry de Leyer had always known, the end of Snowman's quest for glory, the end of his job at The Knox School, the end of Hollandia Farm. The doctor had tried to appear hopeful, but Harry knew he had grave doubts that the cancer could be cured. Finally they started talking, because there were many things that had to be done very soon.

They talked about selling the horses and about ways for living after Harry stopped earning money from The Knox School and from the horse farm. Snowman was, of course, an asset which would bring in quite a nice sum of money—nothing like the amount he could be sold for if he was allowed to win a national championship, but still a large amount. Harry was sure Oak Ridge stables would like to own the big gray. As they rode along, Harry kept thinking about Snowman. It would be tough to part with him. If Chef were older he'd be able to carry on, but he wasn't and wouldn't be for a long time.

When they were halfway home Harry turned to Johanna. "Let's go to Smithtown and see the show," he said.

"I'd like that," Johanna answered. She had a feeling that watching Snowman jump would help to ease the black worries which had descended upon Harry.

As they drove to Smithtown, they talked about buyers for the horses, discussed people who would be interested in Wayward Wind and Pedro, a new colt Johanna was training. The show horses would sell readily, but the riding horses would require time, and the ponies would bring in little money. Johanna did not suggest that she carry on with the horse farm. Harry would need her care if things went badly, and she had the children to look after. Harry knew that going to Smithtown was mostly an escape from the necessity of breaking the news to the children, especially Chef and Harriet. The horses were very

much a part of their young lives. He decided they would keep
two for a while.

They reached the show grounds and found a place in the
bleachers, avoiding the few people they knew who were present. Harry made no attempt to go down to the paddock to see
Snowman. His grooms were there; Snowman would be carefully
cared for. He'd have to get used to not seeing the gray gelding
before a contest, to not handling him, scratching his neck to
make him roll up his lip. There were a hundred small things he'd
have to get used to missing.

They were in time for the open-jumper event. As Harry
watched the jumpers come out for their rounds he felt a hard

lump form inside him. Jumpers were his life, and that life would soon be over. Andante pranced in with Dave Kelly riding her. She whirled about, close to the fence, and headed toward the first jump, a graceful fleeting creature who seemed to rise and float over the barrier. She went on in a small scattering of dust and had a fine round with only two faults. Snowman would have to be at his best to outpoint her.

The big gray gelding trotted through the gate. Dave Kelly swung him around. In spite of Dave's firm rein Snowman turned his head to look at the people along the fence, then upward toward the bleachers as though searching for a familiar face. Johanna took a deep breath and clenched her hands in her lap. Harry leaned forward, his eyes on the big gray. He felt a strong urge to call out to Snowman.

Snowman headed toward the first barrier. Harry closed his hands into fists. He wanted the big fellow to make a fine showing on this, his last time out carrying the De Leyer colors. Snowman took the first barrier clean. Dave was riding him as nearly as possible the way Harry rode him, giving the gray a light rein, stretching forward along the gray neck as Harry did, letting him take over at each jump. He swung along over the coop, wall, brush rail, barrels, the target—over them all he went, jumping high and easy and clean. He took the last barrier—brush rails—with a smooth upward thrust of his big body, and pounded on to a clean victory. Inside his hands Harry's palms were damp with sweat. He felt a great emptiness inside him, but he was grateful to Dave Kelly for riding the gray gelding to a victory over his own cherished Andante. He turned to Johanna.

"I guess we can go now," he said.

Before they could rise, the public address system began making an announcement. "Mr. Harry de Leyer is wanted at home at once. An emergency at the home of Mr. Harry de Leyer." The message was repeated as Johanna and Harry got hurriedly to their feet and started making their way down out of the bleachers.

What had happened at home? Had an accident happened to one of the children? Had there been a fire? The best way to find out was to rush home. They ran to the parking lot and got into the station wagon. Harry started it and swung it around, then roared out along the highway.

As they turned in at Hollandia Farm's gate they were relieved to see no sign of a fire. Everything in the yard and at the stable seemed peaceful, but none of the children were in sight. Johanna jumped out of the car and ran toward the house with Harry close behind her. The kitchen door was open, and they burst inside as the startled neighbor woman, who was caring for the children, turned from the sink where she had been washing dishes.

"My, you startled me!" she exclaimed.

"The children, are they here?" Johanna cried as she looked about and started for the living room.

The neighbor woman nodded and smiled. "They are down in the playroom." She turned to Harry. "There was a call from your doctor. He said it was urgent, and for you to call him as soon as you came in."

Both Johanna and Harry relaxed. They were so relieved over the news that Harry delayed going into the living room to phone.

"That's wonderful," Johanna said. "I mean about the children being safe." She looked at Harry. He smiled at her.

"It can't be anything very bad." His smile faded. "We've had all of the bad news that doctor can give us."

He walked into the living room and crossed to the phone stand, seated himself, and searched in a pocket for the card with the doctor's number on it. Johanna came to the door and hesitated. She wanted to slip down to the playroom just to look at Chef, Harriet, and Marty, but she was also interested in the call.

Harry dialed and waited. The doctor's receptionist answered.

Harry said, "This is Harry de Leyer. I understand the doctor wishes to speak to me."

"Yes, Mr. de Leyer. I'll put the doctor on." The receptionist's voice sounded excited. Harry frowned and waited.

"Harry?" The doctor seemed glad to have found Harry.

"Yes," Harry said.

"Good news, Harry. The laboratory made a mistake on your tissue analysis. They got it mixed up with another report. Your tumor was not malignant."

Harry sat staring at the phone. Johanna rushed across the room. The doctor's voice came over the wire.

"Did you hear me, Harry? You do not have a malignant tumor."

"I heard you," Harry said. "Thanks." He dropped the receiver into place and slowly swung around to face Johanna.

"What is it?" Johanna said in a worried voice. Harry's face looked so blank that she was frightened.

Harry suddenly started laughing. Then he stopped and got to his feet. This was something that could happen only in real life; no storyteller would ever use such a fantastic trick.

"I don't have cancer," Harry said. "That laboratory sent the doctor somebody else's tissue report." The eagerness faded momentarily. "Tough on somebody."

For a long minute they stood looking at each other, readjusting their patterns of thought and feeling which had sent them into the depths of despair, feeling the numbness in them melt away to be replaced by a surge of happiness.

"You don't have cancer," Johanna whispered.

"I don't have anything wrong with me," Harry said. "I feel wonderful."

In a moment they were in each other's arms, their lives given back to them, the future again colored by a rosy glow.

9 Jump, Boy, Jump!

HARRY DE LEYER'S life had been given back to him, and the gift seemed to spur him to greater effort than ever before. The grooms brought Snowman back to Hollandia Farm, along with the blue ribbon Dave Kelly had accepted for him. There was a happy rush to get the gray gelding ready for Stony Brook. News that Harry de Leyer was seriously ill got around when Dave Kelly rode Snowman at Smithtown, and there were many calls. Harry was made to realize that he was known and liked, also that the big gray had a host of friends who wanted to see him go on and win. There was also talk about Dave Kelly's riding the gray to beat his own mare, Andante. Wise people knew what that meant to Dave.

The horse crowd knew that Andante was Dave Kelly's love and pride. She was a dangerous horse to ride, willful and wild and unpredictable. Only Dave Kelly could make her perform in championship form. Snowman had taken every important trophy from her since he entered the shows. Harry knew how Dave felt and was eager for a chance to repay him, though he was aware that he'd never be able to make it up to Dave. He also knew that Snowman would go on beating Andante.

The tongue was no problem at all. It was healing fast, and Harry was regaining lost weight and strength. Having come to know what a man can lose, Harry plunged into the activities of Hollandia Farm and into the many chores which need doing in order to keep a jumper in form for the horse-show circuit. Points became almost an obsession with him. He wanted to enter Madison Square Garden with at least part of the national honors won—the Professional Horsemen's Association trophy, known as the P.H.A.

Harry's expenses were heavy, and the purses were not big. There were no hundred-thousand-dollar purses. This was a rich man's sport. No champion was expected to pay his way, except those sold to a fancier who wanted a blue-ribbon winner. But Harry soon discovered that not only was Snowman going to collect ribbons, but he was also going to pay his way if he kept on taking the big prize of each show, with its five-hundred-to-a-thousand-dollar purse.

Hollandia had other jumper interests besides Snowman, but the big gray was the central interest at the De Leyer stable, the real heart of it, in a manner of speaking. Harry had Pedro whom he had picked up as a discard. To begin with, Pedro had looked like a lank scrub colt even though he did have good bloodlines. He had not been judged worth training as a hunter or a jumper. He was just the sort of horse Harry was always interested in, the kind he liked to buy.

Johanna had taken a special interest in Pedro from the start, and it was soon understood that she would give him most of his

training. Harry kept an eye on the horse as he came along and worked him at times, but it was Johanna who sleeked him up and put him over the practice barriers. Pedro was different in temperament from Snowman. When he swung through the gate and onto the course, people noticed his proud stride, the way he showed off as he floated along. And float is the best word to describe his easy, flowing gait. He was a great horse, and in 1958 he was on the De Leyer team.

There was also Wayward Wind, who was making a name for herself—a beautiful mare, and one on which Harry lavished special training when she was coming along. The trim mare was destined for greatness.

And there was Night Arrest. Harry stabled and worked her because Luisa, at The Knox School, could not handle her. In fact, no one but Harry de Leyer would ride Night Arrest. Harry rode her, and he won ribbons with her.

But Snowman wasn't neglected, not that caring for him called for much fuss. No one had to soothe any temperamental out-bursts or fits of nervousness. He didn't have to be worked hard to keep him from getting restless or mean; all he asked was at-tention and notice from Harry, and room to gallop and kick up his heels between shows. One thing that was done was to raise the paddock fence and gate. If Snowman got a whiff of greener pastures or wooded slopes he was apt to decide to go roaming. When that spirit hit him he just jumped the fence and was off. Harry finally got his fences and gates at a height that discouraged the big gray, even though he liked his barriers high. But as the days went by, he began to lose his wanderlust. Life was just too sweet at Hollandia Farm.

The Stony Brook, Long Island, show was to start September fifth. Snowman was now well along in the circuit. His power and staying qualities were beginning to pay off. He could go the route week after week, whereas a less powerful horse would have to be held back and saved for the big events. He could and did jump at two shows being held on the same dates. He seemed tireless, indestructible, but Harry was to discover that Snowman did have his limits.

The first day of the Stony Brook show was, as it had been at so many shows that summer, a Harry de Leyer day. He rode Wayward Wind in the green-jumper class, and the sleek mare won the first-place blue with almost a perfect round. This was her first season, of course, but she looked like a horse that would be able to compete in the tougher events to come.

Harry followed Wayward Wind's victory with a win on Night Arrest, a knock-down-and-out in a very good field of jumpers. As usual Night Arrest had to be handled firmly, curbed just right at every barrier, kept constantly under a tight rein. It was tough, grueling work for Harry de Leyer, but he didn't mind.

To make the day perfect Harry had to take the open-jumper stake on Snowman. They came through the gate, with Snowman taking an interest in everybody, as usual. He tossed his head and pricked his ears forward as the crowd applauded. No longer was the gray gelding taking second place to the thoroughbreds in the affection of a crowd. Harry had a feeling that the big gray wasn't thinking about barriers at all. He never seemed to notice one until he found it in his path. He swung around, took a glance at the brush rail across from him, headed toward it at an easy gallop, and cleared it cleanly, then galloped on, leaping over rail, fence, the hog's back, on and up and over every barrier, then away to his stall, with the crowd cheering.

But later on in the show, Snowman did not do so well with the knock-down-and-out. He started out jumping clean but when he came to the triple bars his timing was bad. He didn't get off the ground right, and rails went flying, faulting him out of the event. At first Harry suspected that his easy victories were making him careless. He talked sternly to the big gray as he rode him back to his stall.

But when he unsaddled him he found Snowman was sweating and actually trembled. He didn't appear to have a fever. Harry checked and found his temperature was normal. As he blanketed the big gray he began to wonder whether the killing pace he had set for the big fellow was catching up with him. This was a critical time in the series of shows. Snowman had to stay in and battle.

When the De Leyer caravan reached Hollandia Farm, Harry gave his attention to Snowman. He was sure it wasn't medicine the big gray needed. One thing Harry could do, and he did it. He strapped a blanket on Snowman and wrapped his legs in bandages, then put him in his stall. He was worried when Snowman didn't show much interest in grain or hay. Perhaps he had burned the jumper out, something he had always been careful to guard against. Snowman's placid lack of temperament and his willingness had likely kept Harry from noticing what was happening.

Harry didn't sleep well that night. His worry was shared by Johanna, Harriet, and Chef as well as the two grooms. After tossing about for a long time, Harry finally went to sleep, and overslept in the morning. The pace he was holding was telling on him, too.

So Harry wasn't the first to see Snowman in the morning. One of the grooms awakened just after daylight had brought dawn to the farm. He thought at once about Snowman. He almost hated to go and look at the big horse. He didn't want to find him down in his stall. But he went, moving around the sheds to the paddock.

The groom halted at the gate and stared into the training lot, his eyes popping. Snowman was out in the paddock, and he didn't look sick or tired. As the groom stepped to the gate the big gray galloped toward a practice barrier and leaped over it, bandaged legs flashing, blanket flapping in the wind. He wheeled and kicked up his heels, then circled the paddock and returned to his stall in the stable. The groom turned and ran to the house.

Harry was up and dressed when the groom knocked on the back door. He was irritated because he had overslept. He opened the door and looked at the excited young man standing there. "Snowman," the groom said. Harry cut in tersely.

"Is he down?"

"Down? No, he was out in the paddock taking jumps." The groom grinned. "He sure looked funny in those bandages and that blanket."

Harry relaxed. He had a feeling that the groom was coloring his story quite a bit, but it was good news if Snowman was just feeling good. They hurried out to the stable.

Snowman was in his stall, and he nickered eagerly when Harry spoke to him. His appetite had returned; he wanted oats and hay. Harry stepped into the stall and slid a hand under the blanket. Snowman's gray coat was damp; he had certainly been taking exercise. Harry laughed. Perhaps the groom had seen the gray gelding leaping over practice jumps. He often did by himself when he was feeling especially lively.

The next show was Piping Rock, which started September twelfth, and would certainly be the toughest competition so far for the big gray. The twelve-jump Olympic course was rugged enough to test the strength and endurance of any jumper.

The field included such famous jumpers as Diamant and Kzar d'Esprit, of the U. S. Equestrian team; Dave Kelly's three-time winner of "the horse of the year award," Andante; Betty Bosley's Virginia champion, Smithareens; Rudy Smithers's star jumper from California; and many others—all well known. Marie Lafrenz picked Snowman to win and said so a number of times in her column. George Coleman liked Diamant and said so in big type. The majority of the writers favored Diamant, who had a big edge in experience from past shows.

Vanning in and getting settled was old stuff by now for the De Leyer clan. Wooden shoes were put on, and overalls replaced dress clothes. There was work for all except Marty, and they made a game out of the whole thing. Harry worked in the stall in coveralls until show time. And now Johanna and Harriet had ribbons to tack up on the wall beside Snowman's stall. The DeLeyer stable area had plenty of ribbons to flutter in the wind between the three stalls. With everything made snug, Harry got into his riding clothes and boots. He made a last check of everything. Bales of hay were stacked, the grain sack tied securely, the camp stools in place. The family sat and let the barn smells eddy around them. Presently Chef, Harriet, and Marty hurried off to get good places at the fence. After Piping Rock, their school attendance would interfere with show-going, except for shows held on weekends.

In the first open-jumper event of the day, only two horses had clean records over the stiff course. Snowman and Diamant went around clean. The barriers were raised. Snowman seemed to perk up as he faced jumps more to his liking. He had another clean round; Diamant had one fault.

Snowman was now in the lead for the championship and the Blitz Gold Cup, which was scored on the total points earned in all of the open-jumper events. This award carried a thousand dollars in cash along with the cup. Not all of the jumpers were entered in the twelve-jump course. No one expected the jumpers to go clean on this second contest, which was tougher than the one Snowman had won earlier. But Snowman did and so did a horse named Sonora.

The rails went up. Harry knew that Snowman must be tiring. No horse could have gone through what he had and remain fresh. Sonora had not competed in the opening rounds and would be in

better shape. Snowman went first, and Harry felt his heart sink as the gray gelding cleared the last barrier. There were just twenty-four feet between the heightened gate and the final aiken. Over that last barrier Snowman had faulted, bringing his total faults to four for the round.

Sonora came through the gate, riden by Oak Ridge's rider, Adolph Mogavaro. It looked as though Mrs. James Nessler's jumper would be able to outpoint Harry de Leyer's eighty-dollar plow horse. The gelding took the jumps eagerly and with swift grace. Adolph Mogavaro is an expert rider. He used every trick he knew to get Sonora to jump high and clean. At the last barrier Sonora collected a fault, just as Snowman had done, which brought his total to four. They were again tied. The rails would go up again for a third jump-off. This is the sort of pressure that tests the heart of a jumper. It would mean the equivalent of a thirty-six-jump course without rest between rounds. But this would be the last round; now time for the course counted as well as faults. If there were equal faults, the fastest horse would win. That settled the issue for the crowd. Against the fleet Sonora, a big farm horse who never seemed to exert himself wouldn't have a chance.

Harry swung Snowman around and sent him at the first barrier. He was aware that he had to use every riding trick he knew; he had to cut corners for time; no wide sweeps or easy turns; Snowman had to cut corners. As the big gray came down over the first jump, Harry firmly pulled his head around so that he would take the shortest possible distance to the next jump. As they closed on the three rails he leaned forward along the gray neck and spoke to Snowman. "High, boy, high."

Snowman cleared the barrier and pounded on. At the brush rails, which loomed dangerously high and wide, he again leaned forward and spoke to the big gray. "Up, Teddy bear, up." That was his favorite name for the gray gelding. Snowman went up high and wide, but he collected a fault. They swung into the final line of barriers, and Snowman picked up speed like a farm horse who is headed for the barn after a long day's work in the fields. As he leaped and went over the last jump, he collected his fourth fault. The judges jotted down his time as he trotted away to his stall. It was fifty-four seconds.

Adolph Mogavaro guided Sonora through the gate and swung the gelding around. He had a choice to make. He could let Sonora out or he could curb him enough to try for fewer faults than Snowman had collected. He chose the safer way. He was sure that, even curbed, Sonora was faster than the big gray.

Mogavaro tapped Sonora lightly on his rump, and the sleek jumper flashed toward the first barrier, went up and over cleanly. He flashed on, making magnificent jumps over the high barriers, but he collected four faults in the round. Silence held the crowd as the judges checked the time sheets. Then the public address system announced, "Harry de Leyer's Snowman four faults. Time: fifty-four seconds. Mrs. James Nessler's Sonora four faults. Time: fifty-nine seconds."

Snowman had done it again. There was a great roar from the crowd and prolonged hand clapping. It had been a close finish, with Harry de Leyer's skill furnishing the winning margin of five seconds. Now Snowman had sixteen points, an eight-point lead over Diamant. It was not a lead that assured him victory, but it did give him an edge.

The strain of the contests began to tell on both horses and riders. Now breeding and heart began to tell. Snowman had no breeding behind him that anyone knew about, but he had plenty of heart—sometimes known as *bottom*. Diamant picked up points, and it began to look as though the big German horse might be able to jump his way to the Blitz championship. Snowman held a steady pace and made points, but Diamant passed him and was five points ahead when they came to the final all-important round.

The horses came out for the final open-jumper event. None of them went clean until Snowman posted a perfect round. Diamant came on with power equal to that of the gray gelding and with a great deal more experience. He started strong and jumped with class, but he knocked off one pole when halfway through the course. Snowman was Blitz champion, and a thousand dollars was added to his season's earnings.

In the green-jumper class Night Arrest met a horse she could

not beat and had to settle for second place to Windsor Castle, a mare who became a champion several years later. She was a mare Harry de Leyer could have owned; she was so clearly championship class from the beginning that she offered no challenge to Harry.

Harry de Leyer was now being called the Flying Dutchman by the press. His story and Snowman's story had been repeated in the papers over and over. The De Leyer clan took the publicity in their stride. They had their faces turned toward Madison Square Garden. Harry had no time for chatter with the press or admirers. If a writer wanted to talk to him he could do it at the stalls while Harry checked his tack or groomed a horse or forked litter out of a stall. Harry was willing to talk so long as it didn't interfere with his work. Hollandia Stable was run on a limited budget for help.

It had been a gypsy summer. It would go on, but there would be a slight change. Chef and Harriet had to be in school except on weekends. But they would be excused if Snowman reached the Garden. So the De Leyer caravan moved on to Paramus, Harrisburg, Washington. Snowman met and mastered every obstacle, every pattern of course. He won a high-jumper contest, the toughest test a jumper can face. The high-jump course is usually over a six-barrier run. The barriers are sloping poles laid one above the other and calling for a high, wide leap. The first jump is three feet eight, and the height increases to five feet. This sort of course suited Snowman, and he showed his best form when he faced the six hurdles. Harry was soon convinced that Snowman could do things no other jumper could accomplish. Past and forgotten was the worry that Snowman would tire and burn out. Snowman was the strongest horse Harry had ever known. He had the power and he conserved it by not being temperamental or nervous.

Of course, the basis for his success was his placid plow-horse nature. He was no high-strung bundle of energy; he was a machine powered by strong muscles, guided by a clear brain. And his sense of humor never deserted him. In a way he became a bit of a show-off, but if ever a horse had earned the right to show off a little, it was Snowman. If he had been a human actor the crowds would have spoiled him. He was the darling of every show he entered. Thousands got to know him. When he trotted out on a course he got an ovation such as no jumper before him had ever known.

In Washington, the last show before the Garden, Snowman faced a high-jump course as the last event of the show. As he had always done, he had picked up points through the show, and, as a final gesture to the season's circuit, he was facing the high

jumps against a selected field—the few jumpers who could master the sloping pole barriers.

Snowman came out as fourth horse. The three before him had collected faults. The course was slippery with mud, making the jumps dangerous hazards. Snowman did not mind the mud; he was used to sloppy, slippery ground by now. But when he went into the five-foot jump he skidded, one of his hind feet hitting sloping ground. He went crashing into the poles and fell, rolling over in the mud. Harry was thrown clear, and also rolled, much farther than Snowman. It was the first time the big gray had ever been down. Harry scrambled up out of the mud, but Snowman was on his feet before Harry reached him. He stood staring at the wrecked barrier, an astonished look on his face. Then, with a snort, he turned his back upon the poles. He appeared disgusted because he had come a cropper over a five-foot barrier. Harry led him away, keeping a close watch for a limp or any other sign of injury. Snowman plodded along at an easy walk. The fall hadn't even stirred him up.

Snowman appeared to be indestructible. Marie Lafrenz, of the *New York Herald Tribune*, was now a loyal fan of the gray gelding. She never missed a show if it was at all possible, and she left no doubt about what horse she thought would win in the Garden. George Coleman, of the *Sun*, still didn't think the gray plow horse could possibly top the big show. His faith was still with the thoroughbreds. Most of the others writers hedged their bets by saying Snowman was a serious contender.

So Harry de Leyer's old eighty-dollar horse headed for Madison Square Garden with a happy clan of De Leyers trooping along to support him and cheer him on. The youngsters brought along their blue jackets, symbol of the De Leyer stable, sure they would get to parade in them when the awards were passed out.

The event of the year was just ahead. Among five hundred horses entered in every class, Snowman would contend for open-jumper honors. It would be a long heartbreaking eight-day contest, piled on top of a season of grinding circuit shows. Horses that had been nursed along especially for this show would be fresh and eager. But nothing worried the De Leyer clan. They had boundless faith in their eighty-dollar horse.

10 | The Curtain Rises

MADISON SQUARE GARDEN: the seventy-fifth annual National Horse Show—running from November fourth through November eleventh. On the afternoon of the third the De Leyer caravan arrived at the stuffy quarters where horses would be stabled. Here was none of the fresh country air they had known all summer and fall. They had entered the cavernous canyons of a great city where the rattle and clang of traffic took the place of the voice of the wind in tall trees and the night choruses from pond and stream. In place of the frog chorus there was the angry shrilling of auto horns, rising above the roar and rattle of moving monsters, like voices of despair. Here there were no bridle paths, just wide expanses of pavement being pounded day and night by rubber tires, streets having long forgotten the impact of a shod hoof.

But the De Leyers were happy, excited, and eager to get on
with the show. Johanna and Harriet set about making the stall
area a gala place. Snowman now had enough gay ribbons to
cover a whole wall. They tacked them up, then set out camp
stools, put the lunch basket in the shade, and brought a jug of
lemonade from the pickup truck. Chef and Marty tacked the
lettered sign SNOWMAN to the lower half of his stall door.
Harry and the two grooms cared for the horses, broke open
bales of hay and measured out grain. The stall floors were well
littered with straw. Stables like Oak Ridge, where Dave Kelly
had twenty-nine grooms, did not expect the trainers or rider to
fork out litter or wrestle with bales of hay. The De Leyer operation was a dirty-hands job; everybody pitched in and did what
needed to be done.

And the little group felt like David. Their weapons against
the giants were faith—the weapon of David—and Snowman.
That was all they felt they needed to win.

In addition to Snowman, Harry was riding Night Arrest and
Belle Amie, who had been coming along strong during the latter
part of the season, jumping beautifully, winning ribbons. The
wild little mare, Night Arrest, did not like New York's sounds
and smells. The roar of the city and the smell of air laden with
exhaust fumes made her jumpy and irritated. There was no way
of knowing how she would react to the lights and the confine-
ment of the Garden. But Harry was confident that he could
handle her. He had done it on other very trying occasions.

Grooms, handlers, and spectators paused to look at Snowman
and his mass of fluttering ribbons. Some were curious and just
wanted a close look at the fabulous eighty-dollar horse who had
come in from farm fields to challenge the country's best
thoroughbreds.

The professionals—among them an occasional rider—were
curious, too. Here was a phenomenon, almost a freak. But when
they stepped close to the stall and looked at the fine head with

its Arabian ears and its intelligent eyes, they knew that here was a horse to be reckoned with. Those who had competed against Snowman on the horse-show circuits and had met him on other stable streets stopped for a word with Johanna and Harry, a friendly "good luck," spoken sincerely. They also had a friendly word and pat for the gray gelding. He was that kind of a horse.

The seventy-fifth National Horse Show was different in one way from those that had come before it. The difference was in the crowd. The other crowds had been appreciative but decorous; the 1958 crowd was volatile and vocal, ready and eager to clap and stamp and shout. They cheered the harness and gaited classes and roared their approval of the International Teams on parade. It was as though the Garden had inherited a lot of Dodger fans.

On the first morning, there was close to a riot when a group of ill-advised patriots broke into the circle where the International Teams were being presented and photographed. The invaders were out to scream angry imprecations at the Cuban Team. Police quickly banished the hecklers. The crowd applauded loudly, but no one knew whether they were cheering for the Cubans or for the hecklers, and no one cared.

Harry had stayed at his stable cleaning stalls, grooming Snowman, and exercising him in the training paddock across the street from the stables. The grooms worked Night Arrest and Belle Amie. Johanna and the children were off at ten-thirty to get good seats for the gala opening at eleven o'clock. Harry would arrive a little before eleven for the open-jumper event.

Chef, Harriet, and Marty were hopping with excitement by the time the Army band started playing for the march of the International Teams. Then the band played the national anthem of each country's team, and everyone stood up in respectful silence. It was the only silence the Garden was to have for eight days. There wasn't even a boo or a catcall when the Cuban anthem was played. Everyone was in a happy, amiable mood.

The Canadian Royal Mounted Police, seated on black horses, paraded in their scarlet uniforms. They did an intricate drill before galloping off. Their color added to the brightness of the scene.

The open-jumper contest would be a hot one because no one dared to risk staying out and losing a chance at points. Snowman would be meeting many horses he had jumped against before as well as many who had come from far away. Oak Ridge Stables would have a double threat in First Chance and Sonora, both ridden by Adolph Mogavaro. Dave Kelly would be there with Andante. The Saxon Woods Farm had entered Saxon Wood, who had won the 1957 Reserve Championship. Eleo Sears had entered Diamant and Kzar d'Esprit. Dave Kelly was also riding Sam Magid's Little David, a fiery little jumper who had been known to stage a number of upsets. Two of the nation's best-known women riders were out to take the prize away from the men: Betty Bosley was riding her jumper The Clown, and Shirleye Weinstein was riding a winner, Bellaire, a former jumper with the Canadian team. One great horse would be absent— Riviera Wonder, who had won all of the Garden honors in the past three shows. He was retired because of injury. It would have been gray against gray if Riviera Wonder had been able to compete against Snowman. The list of entries was long, and every horse on it had won the right to jump in the big show. The list would be cut down by elimination to the top contenders, fifteen in number.

As the spirited jumpers came out they showed their reactions to the noisy crowd; some fought their riders, others shied and danced as their riders maneuvered them into position for the first barrier. When Snowman's turn came, he trotted placidly out onto the course and looked around at the masses of people in the stands and boxes. He seemed a bit disappointed because there was no fence with children perched upon its top rail. Many of the people were circuit-show followers and knew the gray gelding. Most of the others had read stories about him and knew the history of Harry de Leyer's eighty-dollar plow horse. If they read the sports pages they knew all about the Flying Dutchman as well as his horse. They roared their delighted approval, and Snowman shook his head at them.

The first barrier was a pole-over-grass bank. Snowman took it easily and went on over white poles where he turned right into natural split rails. The course was compact with many turns, made necessary by the criss-crossing of the layout to make it fit the Garden's space. Snowman cleared a high stone wall, more white poles, and sailed over the last barrier with only two faults for the round. He placed second, Diamant winning the blue ribbon.

Harry and his horses rested during the afternoon. Johanna and the children watched the International Jumping event, which started off as a duel between the American and the German teams. Chef clapped and shouted, rooting for the American team. Marty did not get really excited until the famous Budweiser Clydesdales came prancing in, pulling a gaily colored beer wagon. He was wild about the eight huge horses—eight tons of horseflesh, as each weighs a ton. Their white feet and legs pranced in unison; their heads were up and alert as they moved through a wagon drill. Chef and Harriet joined Marty in cheering before the drill was over. The Clydesdales reminded Johanna of the big draft horses she had known back in Holland.

At ten o'clock that night Harry was riding both Snowman and Night Arrest in the knock-down-and-out jumper event. He was up first on Night Arrest. She reacted badly to the lights and the noisy crowd as she came through the gate. The tight field and the towering stands all round her seemed to terrify her. Harry had to curb her sharply. He wasted no time in turning her and heading her into the first barrier, a four-foot brush-with-rails. As she approached the jump, he had trouble in curbing her to set her for the jump, but she made a clean leap and headed toward the four-foot-six Toronto bank.

A wave of applause rolled down over horse and rider. Night Arrest had class; she was an eye-catcher, clearing barriers with only inches to spare. Harry fought to pull her up and get her set for the Toronto bank, but she seemed to have gone almost mad. She fought her bit and gave a frantic lunge as he closed on the barrier. Harry knew she was going down in a nasty spill. She hit the barrier, and her head went down, her rump and heels up. She staggered but managed to stay on her feet. Harry was thrown, but not clear. With the crowd groaning, she dragged Harry across the hard surface of the course. Being dragged by a galloping horse can be fatal. Harry struggled and finally freed himself. He rolled over as Night Arrest galloped wildly away. Getting to his feet, he dusted himself off and started after his horse. With the help of field attendants, he managed to catch her. The crowd gave him a big hand as he led the mare off the field. He had given them one of the things they had come to see, a bad spill.

Minutes later Harry rode through the gate on Snowman. He was shaken but confident. Snowman shook his head at the crowd, swung around, and headed into the first barrier. He went over the four-foot brush-with-rails, took the Toronto bank, and circled wide to move in on the white gate. He cleared it cleanly but came in on the triple bars at a slight angle. One big hind foot toppled a rail. A groan went up from the crowd. Their favorite had faulted out. It was the same old story; the triple bars were only four foot six inches with a six-foot spread, too easy a jump for the gray gelding to exert himself.

The show hadn't started very well for the De Leyer colors. There wasn't a single happy grin back at the stalls. Harriet was brokenhearted; Chef was grim and grumpy. Only Marty, of the three children, took bad luck in stride. He patted the big gray gelding as though he had won.

"We'll show 'em tomorrow," Chef said grimly.

"We have to," Harriet moaned.

Harry said nothing. He knew that one bad day didn't mean a lost cause. There was still a long way to go before the show was over. Snowman's bad showing might wake the big fellow up and put him on his metal.

The second day of the show had its thrills. There was a three-way tie for second place in the International event, but Snowman furnished the biggest thrill of the day. In the knock-down-and-out event he seemed out to make up for his bad showing of the night before. Along with seven other jumpers, he went clean on the first round. With the rails raised for the jump-off, only two horses went clean—Snowman and First Chance. It was an old story for Harry de Leyer and Adolph Mogavaro. They had met in jump-offs before. This time Adolph was out to even the score. First Chance went clean again. Snowman headed into the first barrier when his turn came. He cleared it high and wide and went on, swinging along unconcerned as could be, galloping to the finish without a fault.

The rails were raised for the third and final jump-off. Now the barriers were a real challenge; one horse would surely fault out or lose on time. First Chance went in strong, but the effort of leaping high and wide was telling. He did not give the fourth barrier enough height and earned a fault. Snowman came on after his minute of rest as unconcerned as ever—so far as the crowd could tell. But Harry had a feeling that there was a change in the way the big gray swung into action. He knew Snowman had increased his speed. He went up high and over the first barrier, then on, pounding along swiftly, going up and over each barrier with plenty of daylight between the rails and his gray belly. He was back in the running, tied with First Chance with eleven points.

There was considerable restrained celebrating at the De Leyer stable that evening, but the children soon went off to bed.

Harry and Johanna followed them within a half hour. The day had been tiring for Harry. The nervous pressure was beginning to build up.

The show went on, with Harry riding his heart out, working his gray gelding as carefully as he knew how. But their combined efforts were not enough. On the fifth day First Chance was ahead. In the first jumper event that day three horses went clean on the first round: Snowman, First Chance, and Douglaston, a jumper who had suddenly begun to show a lot of class. With the rail raised, Snowman again went clean while First Chance knocked down a rail on the sixth barrier and Douglaston toppled one at the fourth jump. First Chance was now only one point ahead of the big gray, but Snowman had enough season points earned to give him the U. S. Challenge Trophy and the Professional Horsemen's Trophy. Snowman might trail by one point, but his popularity had not waned. The crowd went wild every time he set a hoof inside the arena. And outside the Garden he was talked about by taxi drivers, waitresses, businessmen, and just about everyone in the city.

A television station wanted him for a live show in their studio on Fifty-eighth Street. The show would give millions of people a chance to see the farm horse who had made good. Traffic jams stalled the transportation, and so Harry led Snowman down Eighth Avenue to Fifty-eighth Street.

Snowman ambled along the avenue, with truck drivers leaning out of their cabs to ask questions or give advice. Taxi drivers slowed down and craned their necks; the sidewalk traffic snarled up as pedestrians halted to watch a horse move along with the flow of traffic. Harry and Snowman arrived at the studio on time and without mishap.

Snowman took the live show in stride. He was interested in the studio hands, the cameramen, the grips, and the boom men, but he paid no attention to himself as he appeared on the monitor

sets. His interview over, Snowman ambled back up Eighth Avenue.

Snowman went into the final event of the big show with two firsts, two seconds, and two third places. Harry de Leyer's dream was close to fulfillment. He would know shortly after seven forty-five that last evening. Fifteen horses would be selected by elimination to contest for the championship award, and every rider and horse would be jumping to win.

Tired but happy, the De Leyer clan gathered at Snowman's stall early that evening for a loving pat and a word of encouragement for the big gray they loved.

"When he wins we'll all go out and accept the award," Harry said, with a broad smile.

Chef and Harriet beamed up at their father happily; Marty wasn't interested. Johanna laughed.

"Be quite a procession," she said.

"You all stay slicked up, no mussed-up clothes," Harry warned.

That night, as Harry sat in his saddle outside the gate waiting for Snowman's call, he reached forward and scratched Snowman's neck. Snowman curled up his lip in what appeared to be a derisive grin. "You're going to win, old Teddy bear," Harry said.

Minutes later the big gray ambled through the gateway, and trotted into the open space before the first barrier, his tail toward the white four-foot pole-over-brush jump. He lifted his head and turned it as though to acknowledge the wild applause which greeted him. Unhurried, he swung around and headed toward the barrier, his powerful legs swinging him along at a pace which seemed almost lazy. He was on his way to glory. Probably he didn't know it and considered this just another frolic over a lot of obstacles, but he may have sensed it through his closeness to Harry de Leyer, who was keyed up for this supreme test.

Harry leaned along the gray neck as Snowman rose and soared over the pole-over-brush. "Go, boy, go," he said, just loud enough so that his voice reached the forward pricked-up ears. And Snowman went, over the poles and wall—wickers on both sides—height four feet nine inches, on around a wide curve close to the Garden wall, over poles each side of a coop, up and over with space to spare, and on to a four-foot-three white gate with painted poles-over-panels close beyond it. Up and over the wall, with a landing that held his stride, for the two or three steps to the close barrier. His forefeet lifted, and he cleared the tight barrier, then swung away and back into the Liverpool rail-over-brush with ditch. His forefeet lifted over the yawning ditch, and his hind legs thrust like pistons to give him momentum which would carry him high and across the six-foot span. Tail flowing,

hind legs stretched out, he rose and seemed to float over the barrier.

And now the crowd was silent, holding its breath, watching the magnificent old plow horse flying along like the pacing white stallion of legend.

Without breaking stride, the gray gelding circled back to leap over the poles and the wall. He raced on to the white pole-over-brush, taking the jump in stride, swinging back to the painted pole-over-panels, leaping that barrier happily, then racing on again to go over poles each side of the coop, and swinging wide to head for the final jump—five poles-over-coop. Bursting with energy and life, he closed on the barrier and cleared it by a foot.

For a long moment there was silence in the stands; then the crowd went wild. The contest wasn't over, but every person in the stands knew that here was the champion. No jump-off could stop him the way he was jumping that night. None matched his round or came close to matching it. Harry de Leyer proudly rode the big gray out of the Garden, and, as he entered the tunnel leading to the stalls, he leaned over and patted the gray neck and shoulder. No need for words at that moment.

Now there was only the presentation left. The crowd waited impatiently for Harry de Leyer and Snowman to emerge from the tunnel. Every eye was on the dark opening through which Harry would lead the gray gelding. The red carpet was spread; the officials stood in a line, with a lovely lady holding the trophy.

Snowman, in a white blanket, appeared with Harry de Leyer leading him, walking beside him. And fanned out beside Harry came, first Marty, then Harriet, then Chef, and last Johanna. The group moved sedately toward the waiting officials. The boys wore identical blue jackets and dark pants and small bow ties. Harriet wore a belted dress with a flaring skirt. It had white buttons down the front. Johanna was trim in a suit with a fur piece around her neck. The De Leyers looked up into the stands, and they all smiled. The crowd went wild, instantly adding the family to their list of heroes which was headed by Snowman and Harry. Harry had to curb Snowman and wait for the ovation to end. He swung the gray around so that the letters P.H.A. showed plainly along with the legend, CHAMPION 1958 SNOWMAN.

When the trophy was extended to Harry the band struck up a lively number. Snowman came alive, with a jerk of his head which almost sent the trophy flying. He backed off in apparent anger, and Harry had trouble managing him. It was the first time he had ever shown any temperament, and the spectators loved it. A roar of laughter rolled from the stands. Harry de Leyer does not remember what the tune was, but he knows there is certain music the big gray does not like.

The curtain came down on the seventy-fifth anniversary of

the National Horse Show with a big gray plow horse winning two national trophies and the honor of being "horse of the year." The rugged weeks of contesting were over until next season. Harry and Johanna would be guests at dinners; they would be interviewed by reporters; Snowman would go back to Hollandia Farm, where he would keep in shape after a lazy fashion, which was what he had done all through the circuit season.

11 | And Then

DURING the 1959 season Snowman repeated his success of 1958. He won all of the national honors and was "horse of the year." It was the same story over again, a glory trail which ended in Madison Square Garden at the seventy-sixth National Horse Show. In 1960 he bowed to the great mare Windsor Castle, but was reserve champion.

Snowman flew to Harry's and Johanna's home town in Holland and jumped on exhibition there, with both families watching him. The people of St. Oedenrode loved him as much as the people in America do. Chef got a free ride across the Atlantic as groom. He then made a little pocket money by charging boys and girls twenty-five cents for a chance to pat the big gray's neck.

Snowman also traveled to Bermuda for a horse show. There

he competed with many of his former rivals. In Bermuda, Chef rode his pony in competition and started what will probably be a horseman's career.

Harry has talked of retiring the old gray. He's old for a horse, but he does not seem to realize it; he just goes on leaping over barriers and winning contests, jumping in the home paddock, for fun, when he isn't off at Piping Rock, or Sands Point, or some other show.

When he does retire it will be to a new Hollandia Farm, a spacious forty-acre place on Long Island not so very far from the original farm. The new farm has spacious pastures, wooded hills, a large pond, and fine stables. Harry has been offered a hundred thousand dollars for Snowman, but he won't sell the gray gelding who made his dream come true. Snowman will always be a cherished member of the De Leyer clan, which now numbers eight, Harry, Jr., and Andreas having joined the family.